D1095851

The Best of
Dorothy Parker

Introduction by Mervyn Horder
Illustrations by Helen Smithson

THE FOLIO SOCIETY
LONDON 1995

The Best of Dorothy Parker was first published by Methuen in 1952. The text of this selection follows that of the first editon with the addition of 'Big Blonde'.

This edition is reprinted by arrangement with Gerald Duckworth & Co. and Viking Penguin, a division of Penguin Books USA Inc.

Printed on Caxton Wove paper
by St Edmundsbury Press, Bury St Edmunds.
Bound by Hunter & Foulis, Haddington.

Seventh printing 2003

Contents

Illustrations

Introduction

A paradox applying to those artistic creators whose large reputations rest on a very small output is that many of them lived long lives: Catullus was seventy when he died, Duparc, eighty-five, A. E. Housman, seventy-seven and Dorothy Parker, seventy-three. The exiguity of their output has not been due to any brevity of lifespan, but to other reasons.

In the case of Dorothy Parker (1893–1967), her restricted oeuvre is ascribable to the egregious disorder of her life, to her efforts to overcome this disorder with the help of the Scotch bottle, and, perhaps, to the fact that her main creative period was almost exactly that of the Prohibition era in America – 1920–33 – so that the 'Scotch' she was drinking wasn't even the real thing, but inferior bootleg.

A little biography is necessitated by the efflux of time, though her stories and poems have plenty of the autobiographical about them, and a recent film served as a reminder to those (and there are Americans among them) who have forgotten who she was or who have twinned her inextricably in their minds with Ogden Nash. Those who already love her will welcome the fact that she kept up a rapid-fire commentary on her life, which she delivered with mordant relish, and which gives a far more trenchant portrait of her than any approximation by another could possibly do.

Here, then, is Dorothy Parker, as far as possible in her own words.

She was born Dorothy Rothschild on 22 August 1893, two months premature: 'The last time I was ever early for anything.' Her father was not one of the banker Rothschilds; he was a successful Jewish garment manufacturer in New York. Her mother died when she was four, and she was educated at a Catholic convent in the city which 'taught me only that if you spit on a pencil eraser, it will erase ink. I remember little else about it except the smell of the oilcloth and the smell of the nuns' garb.' Of her early poetic efforts, she wrote: 'I have slogged along in the exquisite footsteps of Miss Edna St Vincent Millay, unhappily in my own horrible sneakers. Just a little Jewish girl trying to be cute. Miss Millay did a great deal of harm with her double-burning candles. She made poetry seem so easy that we could all do it – but of course we couldn't.'

She joined *Vanity Fair* in 1917: 'My boss is an idiot, and the rest of the staff is four young men who go to pieces easily. Even when they are in the best of health, you have to stand on their insteps to keep them from flying away.' Fortunately Robert Benchley was to prove her equal. They shared a tiny office: 'An inch smaller and it would have been adultery.'

By 1919, she, Benchley and Robert Sherwood had instituted the famous Round Table lunches at the Algonquin Hotel on West 44th Street. 'It was no Mermaid Tavern, I can tell you. Just a bunch of loudmouths showing off, saving their gags for days, waiting to spring them. The whole thing was made up by people who'd never been there. And may I say they're still making it up?'

She had married, in 1917, when she was twenty-three, an alcoholic stockbroker called Edwin Pond Parker. By 1922 she was separated from him, shrugging off an abortion in the same year with the words: 'It serves me right for putting all my eggs in one bastard.' In the Twenties and early Thirties she tried out several handsome young film stars as lovers, honing her one-liners on them as she went along: 'Ah yes, his is the hue of availability!' 'Poor John, his body went to his head.'

She travelled, too, meeting James Joyce in Paris in 1926 and finding him taciturn: 'He's afraid he might drop a pearl.' In Monte Carlo in the same year she was refused admittance to the casino because she wasn't wearing stockings: 'So I went and found my stockings and then came back and lost my shirt.'

But she also tried four times to commit suicide, sardonically summing up her own incompetence and her subsequent philosophy (though she lost sight of it from time to time) in the famous poem, 'Résumé', to be found on page 147.

In 1928 she gave up her job as book reviewer on the *New*

Yorker on the ground that 'it cut in too much on my reading', and in 1934 she married again – Alan Campbell, an actor eleven years her junior. 'An ideal husband? An English-tailored Greek god, just masterful enough to be entertaining, just wicked enough to be exciting, just clever enough to be a good audience.' They settled in Hollywood, where they floated in and out of matrimony (out in 1947 and 1951, in again in 1950 and 1961) and became as rich as could be expected, given her name and his modest talent. When they were apart she was not unduly concerned: 'Oh, don't worry about Alan. Alan will always fall on somebody's feet.'

She hated Hollywood. Getting an interview with Cecil B. DeMille was, she said, 'like riding a camel through the eye of a needle', and she found it painfully lonely after the camaraderie of the Round Table days: 'Unless someone comes near my office, I'm going to write MEN on the door.'

In 1963 Alan died, and she returned to New York to spend her last years in an obscure hotel: 'the kind of hotel where businessmen install their mothers and then run. My fellow guests take excellent care of themselves, and may look forward to a good twenty years spent doing what they are doing at present, which is nothing at all.'

In the 1950s an English journalist interviewed her there, where she lived alone except for a pet poodle, and found her 'very small, her black hair shingled in the Twenties style. She was wearing a "Bohemian" blouse covered in multi-coloured cross-stitching.' She seemed intensely sad and in need of encouragement, finding it hard to believe that anyone would still be interested in her.

She died in the same hotel in 1967, leaving an estate valued at no more than $20,448 net. Her residuary legatee was The National Association for the Advancement of Colored People.

More, it seems, from a wish to be in the swim than from any deep conviction, Dorothy Parker leaned politically towards the left. She was arrested in 1927 for demonstrating against the trials of Sacco and Vanzetti, two left-wing agitators who were executed – almost certainly wrongly – for a payroll murder. In 1937 she visited Spain during the Civil War: 'The 1930s were progressive days. We thought we were going to make the world better. I forget why we thought it, but we did.'

In Hollywood she helped to found the Hollywood Anti-Nazi League, and, in 1952, during the McCarthy era, found herself under formal investigation by the FBI. Her attitude was characteristic: 'Listen, I can't even get my dog to stay down. Do I look to you like someone who could overthrow the government?' Her comments on her own craft were few and off-hand: 'I haven't got a visual mind. I hear things,' she said. And 'Wit has truth in it. Wisecracking is simply calisthenics with words.' And 'Oh, I said it all right. You know how it is. A joke. When people expect you to say things, you say things. Isn't that the way it is?'

She was always ready to indulge in horseplay with words. Challenged to produce a sentence with the word 'horticulture' in it, she replied instantly: 'You can lead a horticulture, but you can't make her think.' The word 'opium' prompted: 'I opium mother is better today,' while the loss of her garter at a sophisticated New York party was greeted with: 'Nearer my garter Thee.'

Her political involvements did not leave her unscathed and if her instinct for mockery and self-mockery often got the better of her, she was able to realise it. From Spain in 1937, she wrote: 'I heard someone say, and so I said it too, that ridicule is the most effective weapon. I don't suppose I ever really believed it, but it was easy and comforting, and so I said it. Well, now I know. I know that there are things that have never been funny and never will be. And I know that ridicule may be a shield, but it is not a weapon.'

In the *Collected Dorothy Parker*, her work amounted to thirty short stories, two hundred poems and fifty theatre and book reviews. None of the stories exceeds 10,000 words – the length of an average Sherlock Holmes short story. Several, like 'The Lovely Leave' and 'Here We Are', are glorified duologues, and a further five are one-sided telephone conversations or soliloquies. What other writer has achieved such mastery in this exacting genre? – they are superb revue and radio material, requiring the minimum of directorial tampering.

Of the poems, none is more than forty lines long and many of the best are less than ten. They originally appeared in three separate collections, *Death and Taxes*, *Enough Rope* and *Sunset Gun*. Their themes are mostly unrequited or misdirected love and their versification is highly polished – the general effect is of a rather less despondent, female Housman. The brilliance and quotability of her shortest epigrams has unduly overshadowed the merits of some longer and more deeply felt poems: try 'Requiescat' or 'Incurable' for reading aloud.

There are few reviewers, apart from Virginia Woolf, whose words continue to bite so many decades after they were first written – often against the clock. Dorothy Parker's book reviews were highly subjective, showed no scholarship, little literary discernment, and scant evidence of her having read any other books at all apart from those of her declared contemporary heroes, Ring Lardner and Hemingway. Yet the tone of urbane disgruntlement which pervades these pieces gives a satisfaction of its own to the reader.

That, then, is the sum total of her work – an undeniable twentieth-century classic, epitomised by the American wise-crack, underpinned by Jewish melancholy. A clever analyst could no doubt tell you how much or how little her stories and poems owe to the death of her mother when she was four, but it is doubtful if anyone could really explain why they continue to give instant pleasure to so many. We are back with Willa Cather when she wrote about Katherine Mansfield: 'A first-rate writer can only be experienced. It is just the thing in him which escapes analysis that makes him first-rate.'

The Best of Dorothy Parker contains about half her total output – reviews apart. It is a bran-tub for dipping into rather than a major exhibition in any chronological or formal order; but the contents have been carefully chosen to display the full emotional range of which she was capable, from the black diamond glitter of her poems and epigrams to the subtle poignancy of such stories as 'Horsie' or 'Clothe the Naked'.

What it cannot give us is a sense of the epigrammatic commentary which she kept up throughout her life, and on which I have based this introduction. So let us see her off with a further flourish of (her own) trumpets and put on parade a final fanfare of remarks too good to lose.

Actors and actresses were made to be baited: 'Scratch an actor and find an actress,' she said; and she sent a telegram to one of the latter who had finally given birth after many carefully staged appearances during her pregnancy: 'Good work. We all knew you had it in you.' Of an actress who had fallen and broken her leg while working in London, she remarked: 'She must have done it sliding down a barrister,' and of Clare Boothe Luce, said to be very kind to her inferiors, she asked: 'Wherever does she find them?'

'How *do* you do it?' a woman once asked her, to which she replied: 'Ask your analyst; he might have a word with your ovaries.'

'There is no such hour on the present clock as 6.30 NY time. As only New Yorkers know, if you can get through the twilight, you'll live through the night.' She knew a great many twilights, but it did not stop her making her best jokes at her own expense: 'Did I enjoy the party? One more drink and I'd have been under the host.' 'Take me or leave me, or as is the usual order of things, both.'

This is not even what the Irish would call 'the shake of the bag' of her sayings, but it gives an idea of her dangerous charm. 'Brevity is the soul of lingerie, as the petticoat said to the chemise' was one of the earliest slogans she dreamed up while working on *Vanity Fair*: it was also the soul of Parker. And now the book beckons . . .

Mervyn Horder

The Best of Dorothy Parker

ARRANGEMENT IN BLACK AND WHITE

The woman with the pink velvet poppies twined round the assisted gold of her hair traversed the crowded room at an interesting gait combining a skip with a sidle, and clutched the lean arm of her host.

'Now I got you!' she said. 'Now you can't get away!'

'Why, hello,' said her host. 'Well. How are you?'

'Oh, I'm finely,' she said. 'Just simply finely. Listen. I want you to do me the most terrible favour. Will you? Will you please? Pretty please?'

'What is it?' said her host.

'Listen,' she said. 'I want to meet Walter Williams. Honestly, I'm just simply crazy about that man. Oh, when he sings! When he sings those spirituals! Well, I said to Burton, "It's a good thing for you Walter Williams is coloured," I said, "or you'd have lots of reason to be jealous." I'd really love to meet him. I'd like to tell him I've heard him sing. Will you be an angel and introduce me to him?'

'Why, certainly,' said her host. 'I thought you'd met him. The party's for him. Where is he, anyway?'

'He's over there by the bookcase,' she said. 'Let's wait till those people get through talking to him. Well, I think you're simply marvellous, giving this perfectly marvellous party for him, and having him meet all these white people, and all. Isn't he terribly grateful?'

'I hope not,' said her host.

'I think it's really terribly nice,' she said. 'I do. I don't see why on earth it isn't perfectly all right to meet coloured people, I haven't any feeling at all about it – not one single bit. Burton – oh, he's just the other way. Well, you know, he comes from Virginia, and you know how they are.'

'Did he come tonight?' said her host.

'No, he couldn't,' she said. 'I'm a regular grass widow tonight. I told him when I left, "There's no telling what I'll do," I said. He was just so tired out, he couldn't move. Isn't it a shame?'

'Ah,' said her host.

'Wait till I tell him I met Walter Williams!' she said. 'He'll just about die. Oh, we have more arguments about coloured people. I talk to him like I don't know what, I get so excited. "Oh, don't be so silly," I say. But I must say for Burton, he's heaps broader-minded than lots of these Southerners. He's really awfully fond of coloured people. Well, he says himself, he wouldn't have white servants. And, you know, he had this old coloured nurse, this regular old nigger mammy, and he just simply loves her. Why, every time he goes home, he goes out in the kitchen to see her. He does, really, to this day. All he says is, he says he hasn't got a word to say against coloured people as long as they keep their place. He's always doing things for them – giving them clothes and I don't know what all. The only thing he says, he says he wouldn't sit down at the table with one for a million dollars. "Oh," I say to him, "you make me sick, talking like that." I'm just terrible to him. Aren't I terrible?'

'Oh, no, no, no,' said her host. 'No, no.'

'I am,' she said. 'I know I am. Poor Burton! Now, me, I don't feel that way at all. I haven't the slightest feeling about coloured people. Why, I'm just crazy about some of them. They're just like children – just as easygoing, and always singing and laughing and everything. Aren't they the happiest things you ever saw in your life? Honestly, it makes me laugh just to hear them. Oh, I like them. I really do. Well, now, listen, I have this coloured laundress, I've had her for years, and I'm devoted to her. She's a real character. And I want to tell you, I think of her as my friend. That's the way I think of her. As I say to Burton, "Well, for Heaven's sakes, we're all human beings!" Aren't we?'

'Yes,' said her host. 'Yes, indeed.'

'Now this Walter Williams,' she said. 'I think a man like that's a real artist. I do. I think he deserves an awful lot of credit. Goodness, I'm so crazy about music or anything. I don't care *what* colour he is. I honestly think if a person's an artist, nobody ought to have any feeling at all about meeting them. That's absolutely what I say to Burton. Don't you think I'm right?'

'Yes,' said her host. 'Oh, yes.'

'That's the way I feel,' she said. 'I just can't understand people being narrow-minded. Why, I absolutely think it's a privilege to meet a man like Walter Williams. Yes, I do. I haven't any feeling at all. Well, my goodness, the good Lord made him, just the same as He did any of us. Didn't He?'

'Surely,' said her host. 'Yes, indeed.'

'That's what I say,' she said. 'Oh, I get so furious when people are narrow-minded about coloured people. It's just all I can do not to say something. Of course, I do admit when you get a bad coloured man, they're simply terrible. But as I say to Burton, there are some bad white people, too, in this world. Aren't there?'

'I guess there are,' said her host.

'Why, I'd really be glad to have a man like Walter Williams come to my house and sing for us, sometime,' she said. 'Of course, I couldn't ask him on account of Burton, but I wouldn't have any feeling about it at all. Oh, can't he sing! Isn't it marvellous, the way they all have music in them? It just seems to be right *in* them. Come on, let's go on over and talk to him. Listen, what shall I do when I'm introduced? Ought I to shake hands? Or what?'

'Why, do whatever you want,' said her host.

'I guess maybe I'd better,' she said. 'I wouldn't for the world have him think I had any feeling. I think I'd better shake hands, just the way I would with anybody else. That's just exactly what I'll do.'

They reached the tall young Negro, standing by the bookcase. The host performed introductions; the Negro bowed.

'How do you do?' he said.

The woman with the pink velvet poppies extended her hand at the length of her arm and held it so for all the world to see, until the Negro took it, shook it, and gave it back to her.

'Oh, how do you do, Mr Williams,' she said. 'Well, how do you do. I've just been saying, I've enjoyed your singing so awfully much. I've been to your concerts, and we have you on the phonograph and everything. Oh, I just enjoy it!'

She spoke with great distinctness, moving her lips meticulously, as if in parlance with the deaf.

'I'm so glad,' he said.

'I'm just simply crazy about that "Water Boy" thing you sing,' she said. 'Honestly, I can't get it out of my head. I have my husband nearly crazy, the way I go around humming it all the time. Oh, he looks just as black as the ace of – Well. Tell me, where on earth do you ever get all those songs of yours? How do you ever get hold of them?'

'Why,' he said, 'there are so many different — '

'I should think you'd love singing them,' she said. 'It must be more fun. All those darling old spirituals – oh, I just love them! Well, what are you doing, now? Are you still keeping up your singing? Why don't you have another concert, sometime?'

'I'm having one the sixteenth of this month,' he said.

'Well, I'll be there,' she said. 'I'll be there, if I possibly can. You can count on me. Goodness, here comes a whole raft of people to talk to you. You're just a regular guest of honour! Oh, who's that girl in white? I've seen her some place.'

'That's Katherine Burke,' said her host.

'Good Heavens,' she said, 'is that Katherine Burke? Why, she looks entirely different off the stage. I thought she was much better-looking. I had no idea she was so terribly dark. Why, she looks almost like – Oh, I think she's a wonderful actress! Don't you think she's a wonderful actress, Mr Williams? Oh, I think she's marvellous. Don't you?'

'Yes, I do,' he said.

'Oh, I do, too,' she said. 'Just wonderful. Well, goodness, we must give someone else a chance to talk to the guest of honour. Now, don't forget, Mr Williams, I'm going to be at that concert if I possibly can. I'll be there applauding like everything. And if I can't come, I'm going to tell everybody I know to go, anyway. Don't you forget!'

'I won't,' he said. 'Thank you so much.'

The host took her arm and piloted her into the next room.

'Oh, my dear,' she said. 'I nearly died! Honestly, I give you my word, I nearly passed away. Did you hear that terrible break I made? I was just going to say Katherine Burke looked almost like a nigger. I just caught myself in time. Oh, do you think he noticed?'

'I don't believe so,' said her host.

'Well, thank goodness,' she said, 'because I wouldn't have embarrassed him for anything. Why, he's awfully nice. Just as nice as he can be. Nice manners, and everything. You know, so many coloured people, you give them an inch, and they walk all over you. But he doesn't try any of that. Well, he's got more sense, I suppose. He's really nice. Don't you think so?'

'Yes,' said her host.

'I liked him,' she said. 'I haven't any feeling at all because he's a coloured man. I felt just as natural as I would with anybody. Talked to him just as naturally, and everything. But honestly, I could hardly keep a straight face. I kept thinking of Burton. Oh, wait till I tell Burton I called him "Mister"!'

Convalescent

How shall I wail, that wasn't meant for weeping?
Love has run and left me, oh, what then?
Dream, then, I must, who never can be sleeping;
What if I should meet Love, once again?

What if I met him, walking on the highway?
Let him see how lightly I should care.
He'd travel his way, I would follow my way;
Hum a little song, and pass him there.

What if at night, beneath a sky of ashes,
He should seek my doorstep, pale with need?
There could he lie, and dry would be my lashes;
Let him stop his noise, and let me read.

Oh, but I'm gay, that's better off without him;
Would he'd come and see me, laughing here.
Lord! Don't I know I'd have my arms about him,
Crying to him, 'Oh, come in, my dear!'

Experience

Some men break your heart in two,
  Some men fawn and flatter,
Some men never look at you;
  And that cleans up the matter.

The Dark Girl's Rhyme

Who was there had seen us
   Wouldn't bid him run?
Heavy lay between us
   All our sires had done.

There he was, a-springing
   Of a pious race,
Setting hags a-swinging
   In a market-place;

Sowing turnips over
   Where the poppies lay;
Looking past the clover,
   Adding up the hay;

Shouting through the Spring song,
   Clumping down the sod;
Toadying, in singsong,
   To a crabbèd god.

There I was, that came of
   Folk of mud and flame –
I that had my name of
   Them without a name.

Up and down a mountain
   Streeled my silly stock;
Passing by a fountain,
   Wringing at a rock;

Devil-gotten sinners,
   Throwing back their heads;
Fiddling for their dinners,
   Kissing for their beds.

Not a one had seen us
  Wouldn't help him flee.
Angry ran between us
  Blood of him and me.

How shall I be mating
  Who have looked above –
Living for a hating,
  Dying of a love?

A Very Short Song

Once, when I was young and true,
  Someone left me sad –
Broke my brittle heart in two;
  And that is very bad.

Love is for unlucky folk,
  Love is but a curse.
Once there was a heart I broke;
  And that, I think, is worse.

THE SEXES

The young man with the scenic cravat glanced nervously down the sofa at the girl in the fringed dress. She was examining her handkerchief; it might have been the first one of its kind she had seen, so deep was her interest in its material, form, and possibilities. The young man cleared his throat, without necessity or success, producing a small, syncopated noise.

'Want a cigarette?' he said.

'No, thank you,' she said. 'Thank you ever so much just the same.'

'Sorry I've only got these kind,' he said. 'You got any of your own?'

'I really don't know,' she said. 'I probably have, thank you.'

'Because if you haven't', he said, 'it wouldn't take me a minute to go up to the corner and get you some.'

'Oh, thank you, but I wouldn't have you go to all that trouble for anything,' she said. 'It's awfully sweet of you to think of it. Thank you ever so much.'

'Will you for God's sake stop thanking me?' he said.

'Really,' she said, 'I didn't know I was saying anything out of the way. I'm awfully sorry if I hurt your feelings. I know what it feels like to get your feelings hurt. I'm sure I didn't realise it was an insult to say "thank you" to a person. I'm not exactly in the habit of having people swear at me because I say "thank you" to them.'

'I did not swear at you!' he said.

'Oh, you didn't?' she said. 'I see.'

'My God,' he said, 'all I said, I simply asked you if I couldn't go out and get you some cigarettes. Is there anything in that to get up in the air about?'

'Who's up in the air?' she said. 'I'm sure I didn't know it was a criminal offence to say I wouldn't dream of giving you all that trouble. I'm afraid I must be awfully stupid, or something.'

'Do you want me to go and get you some cigarettes; or don't you?' he said.

'Goodness,' she said, 'if you want to go so much, please don't feel you have to stay here. I wouldn't have you feel you had to stay for anything.'

'Ah, don't be that way, will you?' he said.

'Be what way?' she said. 'I'm not being any way.'

'What's the matter?' he said.

'Why, nothing,' she said. 'Why?'

'You've been funny all evening,' he said. 'Hardly said a word to me, ever since I came in.'

'I'm terribly sorry you haven't been having a good time,' she said. 'For goodness' sakes, don't feel you have to stay here and be bored. I'm sure there are millions of places you could be having a lot more fun. The only thing, I'm a little bit sorry I didn't know before, that's all. When you said you were coming over tonight, I broke a lot of dates to go to the theatre and everything. But it doesn't make a bit of difference. I'd much rather have you go and have a good time. It isn't very pleasant to sit here and feel you're boring a person to death.'

'I'm not bored!' he said. 'I don't want to go any place! Ah, honey, won't you tell me what's the matter? Ah, please.'

'I haven't the faintest idea what you're talking about,' she said. 'There isn't a thing on earth the matter. I don't know what you mean.'

'Yes, you do,' he said. 'There's something the trouble. Is it anything I've done, or anything?'

'Goodness,' she said, 'I'm sure it isn't any of my business, anything you do. I certainly wouldn't feel I had any right to criticise.'

'Will you stop talking like that?' he said. 'Will you, please?'

'Talking like what?' she said.

'You know,' he said. 'That's the way you were talking over the telephone today, too. You were so snotty when I called you up, I was afraid to talk to you.'

'I beg your pardon,' she said. 'What did you say I was?'

'Well, I'm sorry,' he said. 'I didn't mean to say that. You get me so balled up.'

'You see,' she said, 'I'm really not in the habit of hearing language like that. I've never had a thing like that said to me in my life.'

'I told you I was sorry, didn't I?' he said. 'Honest, honey, I didn't mean it. I don't know how I came to say a thing like that. Will you excuse me? Please?'

'Oh, certainly,' she said. 'Goodness, don't feel you have to apologise to me. It doesn't make any difference at all. It just seems a little bit funny to have somebody you were in the habit of thinking was a gentleman come to your home and use language like that to you, that's all. But it doesn't make the slightest bit of difference.'

'I guess nothing I say makes any difference to you,' he said. 'You seem to be sore at me.'

'I'm sore at you?' she said. 'I can't understand what put that idea in your head. Why should I be sore at you?'

'That's what I'm asking you,' he said. 'Won't you tell me what I've done? Have I done something to hurt your feelings, honey? The way you were, over the phone, you had me worried all day. I couldn't do a lick of work.'

'I certainly wouldn't like to feel', she said, 'that I was interfering with your work. I know there are lots of girls that don't think anything of doing things like that, but I think it's terrible. It certainly isn't very nice to sit here and have someone tell you you interfere with his business.'

'I didn't say that!' he said. 'I didn't say it!'

'Oh, didn't you?' she said. 'Well, that was the impression I got. It must be my stupidity.'

'I guess maybe I better go,' he said. 'I can't get right. Everything I say seems to make you sorer and sorer. Would you rather I'd go?'

'Please do just exactly whatever you like,' she said. 'I'm sure the last thing I want to do is have you stay here when you'd rather be some place else. Why don't you go some place where you won't be bored? Why don't you go up to Florence Leaming's? I know she'd love to have you.'

'I don't want to go up to Florence Leaming's!' he said.

'What would I want to go up to Florence Leaming's for? She gives me a pain.'

'Oh, really?' she said. 'She didn't seem to be giving you so much of a pain at Elsie's party last night, I notice. I notice you couldn't even talk to anybody else, that's how much of a pain she gave you.'

'Yeah, and you know why I was talking to her?' he said.

'Why, I suppose you think she's attractive,' she said. 'I suppose some people do. It's perfectly natural. Some people think she's quite pretty.'

'I don't know whether she's pretty or not,' he said. 'I wouldn't know her if I saw her again. Why I was talking to her was you wouldn't even give me a tumble, last night. I came up and tried to talk to you, and you just said, "Oh, how do you do" – just like that, "Oh, how do you do" – and you turned right away and wouldn't look at me.'

'I wouldn't look at you?' she said. 'Oh, that's awfully funny. Oh, that's marvellous. You don't mind if I laugh, do you?'

'Go ahead and laugh your head off,' he said. 'But you wouldn't.'

'Well, the minute you came in the room,' she said, 'you started making such a fuss over Florence Leaming, I thought you never wanted to see anybody else. You two seemed to be having such a wonderful time together, goodness knows I wouldn't have butted in for anything.'

'My God,' he said, 'this what's-her-name girl came up and began talking to me before I even saw anybody else, and what could I do? I couldn't sock her in the nose, could I?'

'I certainly didn't see you try,' she said.

'You saw me try to talk to you, didn't you?' he said. 'And what did you do? "Oh, how do you do." Then this what's-her-name came up again, and there I was, stuck. Florence Leaming! I think she's terrible. Know what I think of her? I think she's a damn little fool. That's what I think of her.'

'Well, of course,' she said, 'that's the impression she always gave me, but I don't know. I've heard people say she's pretty. Honestly I have.'

'Why, she can't be pretty in the same room with you,' he said.

'She has got an awfully funny nose,' she said. 'I really feel sorry for a girl with a nose like that.'

'She's got a terrible nose,' he said. 'You've got a beautiful nose. Gee, you've got a pretty nose.'

'Oh, I have not,' she said. 'You're crazy.'

'And beautiful eyes,' he said, 'and beautiful hair and a beautiful mouth. And beautiful hands. Let me have one of the little hands. Ah, look atta little hand! Who's got the prettiest hands in the world? Who's the sweetest girl in the world?'

'I don't know,' she said. 'Who?'

'You don't know!' he said. 'You do so, too, know.'

'I do not,' she said. 'Who? Florence Leaming?'

'Oh, Florence Leaming, my eye!' he said. 'Getting sore about Florence Leaming! And me not sleeping all last night and not doing a stroke of work all day because you wouldn't speak to me! A girl like you getting sore about a girl like Florence Leaming!'

'I think you're just perfectly crazy,' she said. 'I was not sore! What on earth ever made you think I was? You're simply crazy. Ow, my new pearl beads! Wait a second till I take them off. There!'

The Satin Dress

Needle, needle, dip and dart,
Thrusting up and down,
Where's the man could ease a heart
Like a satin gown?

See the stitches curve and crawl
Round the cunning seams –
Patterns thin and sweet and small
As a lady's dreams.

Wantons go in bright brocade;
Brides in organdie;
Gingham's for the plighted maid;
Satin's for the free!

Wool's to line a miser's chest;
Crape's to calm the old;
Velvet hides an empty breast;
Satin's for the bold!

Lawn is for a bishop's yoke;
Linen's for a nun;
Satin is for wiser folk –
Would the dress were done!

Satin glows in candlelight –
Satin's for the proud!
They will say who watch at night,
'What a fine shroud!'

Braggart

The days will rally, wreathing
Their crazy tarantelle;
And you must go on breathing,
But I'll be safe in hell.

Like January weather,
The years will bite and smart,
And pull your bones together
To wrap your chattering heart.

The pretty stuff you're made of
Will crack and crease and dry.
The thing you are afraid of
Will look from every eye.

You will go faltering after
The bright, imperious line,
And split your throat on laughter,
And burn your eyes with brine.

You will be frail and musty
With peering, furtive head,
Whilst I am young and lusty
Among the roaring dead.

Chant for Dark Hours

Some men, some men
Cannot pass a
Bookshop.
(Lady, make your mind up, and wait your life away.)

Some men, some men
Cannot pass a
Crap game.
(He said he'd come at moonrise, and here's another day!)

Some men, some men
Cannot pass a
Bar-room.
(Wait about, and hang about, and that's the way it goes.)

Some men, some men
Cannot pass a
Woman.
(Heaven never send me another one of those!)

Some men, some men
Cannot pass a
Golf course.
(Read a book, and sew a seam, and slumber if you can.)

Some men, some men
Cannot pass a
Haberdasher's.
(All your life you wait around for some damn man!)

THE WALTZ

Why, thank you so much. I'd adore to.

I don't want to dance with him. I don't want to dance with anybody. And even if I did, it wouldn't be him. He'd be well down among the last ten. I've seen the way he dances; it looks like something you do on Saint Walpurgis Night. Just think, not a quarter of an hour ago, here I was sitting, feeling so sorry for the poor girl he was dancing with. And now *I'm* going to be the poor girl. Well, well. Isn't it a small world?

And a peach of a world, too. A true little corker. Its events are so fascinatingly unpredictable, are not they? Here I was, minding my own business, not doing a stitch of harm to any living soul. And then he comes into my life, all smiles and city manners, to sue me for the favour of one memorable mazurka. Why, he scarcely knows my name, let alone what it stands for. It stands for Despair, Bewilderment, Futility, Degradation, and Premeditated Murder, but little does he wot. I don't wot his name, either; I haven't any idea what it is. Jukes, would be my guess from the look in his eyes. How do you do, Mr Jukes? And how is that dear little brother of yours, with the two heads?

Ah, now why did he have to come around me, with his low requests? Why can't he let me lead my own life? I ask so little – just to be left alone in my quiet corner of the table, to do my evening brooding over all my sorrows. And he must come, with his bows and his scrapes and his may-I-have-this-ones. And I had to go and tell him that I'd adore to dance with him. I cannot understand why I wasn't struck right down dead. Yes, and being struck dead would look like a day in the country, compared to struggling out a dance with this boy. But what could I do? Everyone else at the table had got up to dance, except him and me. There was I, trapped. Trapped like a trap in a trap.

What can you say, when a man asks you to dance with him? I most certainly will *not* dance with you, I'll see you in hell first. Why, thank you, I'd like to awfully, but I'm having labour pains. Oh, yes, *do* let's dance together – it's so nice to meet a man who isn't a scaredy-cat about catching my beriberi. No.

There was nothing for me to do, but say I'd adore to. Well, we might as well get it over with. All right, Cannonball, let's run out on the field. You won the toss; you can lead.

Why, I think it's more of a waltz, really. Isn't it? We might just listen to the music a second. Shall we? Oh, yes, it's a waltz. Mind? Why, I'm simply thrilled. I'd love to waltz with you.

I'd love to waltz with you. I'd love to waltz with you. I'd love to have my tonsils out, I'd love to be in a midnight fire at sea. Well, it's too late now. We're getting under way. *Oh.* Oh, dear. Oh, dear, dear, dear. Oh, this is even worse than I thought it would be. I suppose that's the one dependable law of life – everything is always worse than you thought it was going to be. Oh, if I had any real grasp of what this dance would be like, I'd have held out for sitting it out. Well, it will probably amount to the same thing in the end. We'll be sitting it out on the floor in a minute, if he keeps this up.

I'm so glad I brought it to his attention that this is a waltz they're playing. Heaven knows what might have happened, if he had thought it was something fast; we'd have blown the sides right out of the building. Why does he always want to be somewhere that he isn't? Why can't we stay in one place just long enough to get acclimated? It's this constant rush, rush, rush, that's the curse of American life. That's the reason that we're all of us so – *Ow!* For God's sake, don't *kick*, you idiot; this is only second down. Oh, my shin. My poor, poor shin, that I've had ever since I was a little girl!

Oh, no, no, no. Goodness, no. It didn't hurt the least little bit. And anyway it was my fault. Really it was. Truly. Well, you're just being sweet, to say that. It really was all my fault.

I wonder what I'd better do – kill him this instant, with my naked hands, or wait and let him drop in his traces. Maybe it's best not to make a scene. I guess I'll just lie low, and watch the pace get him. He can't keep this up indefinitely – he's only flesh and blood. Die he must, and die he shall, for what he did to me. I don't want to be of the over-sensitive type, but you can't tell me that kick was unpremeditated. Freud says there are no accidents. I've led no cloistered life, I've known dancing partners who have spoiled my slippers and torn my dress; but when it comes to kicking, I am Outraged Womanhood. When you kick me in the shin, *smile*.

Maybe he didn't do it maliciously. Maybe it's just his way of showing his high spirits. I suppose I ought to be glad that one of us is having such a good time. I suppose I ought to think myself lucky if he brings me back alive. Maybe it's captious to demand of a practically strange man that he leave your shins as he found them. After all, the poor boy's doing the best he can. Probably he grew up in the hill country, and never had no larnin'. I bet they had to throw him on his back to get shoes on him.

Yes, it's lovely, isn't it? It's simply lovely. It's the loveliest waltz. Isn't it? Oh, I think it's lovely, too.

Why, I'm getting positively drawn to the Triple Threat here. He's my hero. He has the heart of a lion, and the sinews of a buffalo. Look at him – never a thought of the consequences, never afraid of his face, hurling himself into every scrimmage, eyes shining, cheeks ablaze. And shall it be said that I hung back? No, a thousand times no. What's it to me if I have to spend the next couple of years in a plaster cast? Come on, Butch, right through them! Who wants to live for ever?

Oh. Oh, dear. Oh, he's all right, thank goodness. For a while I thought they'd have to carry him off the field. Ah, I couldn't bear to have anything happen to him. I love him. I love him better than anybody in the world. Look at the spirit he gets into a dreary, commonplace waltz; how effete the other dancers seem, beside him. He is youth and vigour and courage, he is strength and gaiety and – *Ow!* Get off my instep, you hulking peasant! What do you think I am, anyway – a gangplank? *Ow!*

No, of course it didn't hurt. Why, it didn't a bit. Honestly. And it was all my fault. You see, that little step of yours – well, it's perfectly lovely, but it's just a tiny bit tricky to follow at first. Oh, did you work it up yourself? You really did? Well, aren't you amazing! Oh, now I think I've got it. Oh, I think it's lovely. I was watching you do it when you were dancing before. It's awfully effective when you look at it.

It's awfully effective when you look at it. I bet I'm awfully effective when you look at me. My hair is hanging along my cheeks, my skirt is swaddling about me, I can feel the cold damp of my brow. I must look like something out of the 'Fall of the House of Usher'. This sort of thing takes a fearful toll of a woman my age. And he worked up his little step himself, he with his degenerate cunning. And it was just a tiny bit tricky at first, but now I think I've got it. Two stumbles, slip, and a twenty-yard dash; yes. I've got it. I've got several other things, too, including a split shin and a bitter heart. I hate this creature I'm chained to. I hated him the moment I saw his leering, bestial face. And here I've been locked in his noxious embrace for the thirty-five years this waltz has lasted. Is that orchestra never going to stop playing? Or must this obscene travesty of a dance go on until hell burns out?

Oh, they're going to play another encore. Oh, goody. Oh, that's lovely. Tired? I should say I'm not tired. I'd like to go on like this forever.

I should say I'm not tired. I'm dead, that's all I am. Dead, and in what a cause! And the music is never going to stop playing, and we're going on like this, Double-Time Charlie and I, throughout eternity. I suppose I won't care any more, after the first hundred thousand years. I suppose nothing will matter then, not heat nor pain nor broken heart nor cruel, aching weariness. Well. It can't come too soon for me.

I wonder why I didn't tell him I was tired. I wonder why I didn't suggest going back to the table. I could have said let's just listen to the music. Yes, and if he would, that would be the first bit of attention he has given it all evening. George Jean Nathan said that the lovely rhythms of the waltz should be listened to in stillness and not be accompanied by strange gyrations of the human body. I think that's what he said. I think it was George Jean Nathan. Anyhow, whatever he said and whoever he was and whatever he's doing now, he's better off than I am. That's safe. Anybody who isn't waltzing with this Mrs O'Leary's cow I've got here is having a good time.

Still if we were back at the table, I'd probably have to talk to him. Look at him – what could you say to a thing like that! Did you go to the circus this year, what's your favourite kind of ice-cream, how do you spell cat? I guess I'm as well off here. As well off as if I were in a cement mixer in full action.

I'm past all feeling now. The only way I can tell when he steps on me is that I can hear the splintering of bones. And all the events of my life are passing before my eyes. There was the time I was in a hurricane in the West Indies, there was the day I got my head cut open in the taxi smash, there was the night the drunken lady threw a bronze ashtray at her own true love and got me instead, there was that summer that the sailboat kept capsizing. Ah, what an easy, peaceful time was mine, until I fell in with Swifty, here. I didn't know what trouble was, before I got drawn into this *danse macabre*. I think my mind is beginning to wander. It almost seems to me as if the orchestra were stopping. It couldn't be, of course; it could never, never be. And yet in my ears there is a silence like the sound of angel voices . . .

Oh, they've stopped, the mean things. They're not going to play any more. Oh, darn. Oh, do you think they would? Do you really think so, if you gave them twenty dollars? Oh, that would be lovely. And look, do tell them to play this same thing. I'd simply adore to go on waltzing.

I Know I Have Been Happiest

I know I have been happiest at your side;
But what is done, is done, and all's to be.
And small the good, to linger dolefully –
Gaily it lived, and gallantly it died.
I will not make you songs of hearts denied,
And you, being man, would have no tears of me,
And should I offer you fidelity,
You'd be, I think, a little terrified.

Yet this the need of woman, this her curse:
To range her little gifts, and give, and give,
Because the throb of giving's sweet to bear.
To you, who never begged me vows or verse,
My gift shall be my absence, while I live;
But after that, my dear, I cannot swear.

Godspeed

Oh, seek, my love, your newer way;
  I'll not be left in sorrow.
So long as I have yesterday,
  Go take your damned tomorrow!

Testament

Oh, let it be a night of lyric rain
And singing breezes, when my bell is tolled.
I have so loved the rain that I would hold
Last in my ears its friendly, dim refrain.
I shall lie cool and quiet, who have lain
Fevered, and watched the book of day unfold.
Death will not see me flinch; the heart is bold
That pain has made incapable of pain.

Kinder the busy worms than ever love;
It will be peace to lie there, empty-eyed,
My bed made secret by the levelling showers,
My breast replenishing the weeds above.
And you will say of me, 'Then has she died?
Perhaps I should have sent a spray of flowers.'

De Profundis

Oh, is it, then, Utopian
To hope that I may meet a man
Who'll not relate, in accents suave,
The tales of girls he used to have?

The Immortals

If you should sail for Trebizond, or die,
Or cry another name in your first sleep,
Or see me board a train, and fail to sigh,
Appropriately, I'd clutch my breast and weep.
And you, if I should wander through the door,
Or sin, or seek a nunnery, or save
My lips and give my cheek, would tread the floor
And aptly mention poison and the grave.

Therefore the mooning world is gratified,
Quoting how prettily we sigh and swear;
And you and I, correctly side by side,
Shall live as lovers when our bones are bare;
And though we lie forever enemies,
Shall rank with Abelard and Héloïse.

Pictures in the Smoke

Oh, gallant was the first love, and glittering and fine;
 The second love was water, in a clear white cup;
The third love was his, and the fourth was mine;
 And after that, I always get them all mixed up.

THE STANDARD OF LIVING

Annabel and Midge came out of the tea-room with the arrogant slow gait of the leisured, for their Saturday afternoon stretched ahead of them. They had lunched, as was their wont, on sugar, starches, oils, and butter-fats. Usually they ate sandwiches of spongy new white bread greased with butter and mayonnaise; they ate thick wedges of cake lying wet beneath ice-cream and whipped cream and melted chocolate gritty with nuts. As alternates, they ate patties, sweating beads of inferior oil, containing bits of bland meat bogged in pale, stiffening sauce; they ate pastries, limber under rigid icing, filled with an indeterminate yellow sweet stuff, not still solid, not yet liquid, like salve that has been left in the sun. They chose no other sort of food, nor did they consider it. And their skin was like the petals of wood anemones, and their bellies were as flat and their flanks as lean as those of young Indian braves.

Annabel and Midge had been best friends almost from the day that Midge had found a job as stenographer with the firm that employed Annabel. By now, Annabel, two years longer in the stenographic department, had worked up to the wages of eighteen dollars and fifty cents a week; Midge was still at sixteen dollars. Each girl lived at home with her family and paid half her salary to its support.

The girls sat side by side at their desks, they lunched together every noon, together they set out for home at the end of the day's work. Many of their evenings and most of their Sundays were passed in each other's company. Often they were joined by two young men, but there was no steadiness to any such quartet; the two young men would give place, unlamented, to two other young men, and lament would have been inappropriate, really, since the newcomers were scarcely distinguishable from their predecessors. Invariably the girls spent the fine idle hours of their hot-weather Saturday afternoons together. Constant use had not worn ragged the fabric of their friendship.

They looked alike, though the resemblance did not lie in their features. It was in the shape of their bodies, their movements, their style, and their adornments. Annabel and Midge did, and completely, all that young office workers are besought not to do. They painted their lips and their nails, they darkened their lashes and lightened their hair, and scent seemed to shimmer from them. They wore thin, bright dresses, tight over their breasts and high on their legs, and tilted slippers, fancifully strapped. They looked conspicuous and cheap and charming.

Now, as they walked across to Fifth Avenue with their skirts swirled by the hot wind, they received audible admiration. Young men grouped lethargically about news-stands awarded them murmurs, exclamations, even – the ultimate tribute – whistles. Annabel and Midge passed without the condescension of hurrying their pace; they held their heads higher and set their feet with exquisite precision, as if they stepped over the necks of peasants.

Always the girls went to walk on Fifth Avenue on their free afternoons, for it was the ideal ground for their favourite game. The game could be played anywhere, and, indeed, was, but the great shop windows stimulated the two players to their best form.

Annabel had invented the game; or rather she had evolved it from an old one. Basically, it was no more than the ancient sport of what-would-you-do-if-you-had-a-million-dollars? But Annabel had drawn a new set of rules for it, had narrowed it, pointed it, made it stricter. Like all games, it was the more absorbing for being more difficult.

Annabel's version went like this: you must suppose that somebody dies and leaves you a million dollars, cool. But there is a condition to the bequest. It is stated in the will that you must spend every nickel of the money on yourself.

There lay the hazard of the game. If, when playing it, you forgot, and listed among your expenditures the rental of a new apartment for your family, for example, you lost your turn to the other player. It was astonishing how many – and some of them among the experts, too – would forfeit all their innings by such slips.

It was essential, of course, that it be played in passionate seriousness. Each purchase must be carefully considered and, if

necessary, supported by argument. There was no zest to playing wildly. Once Annabel had introduced the game to Sylvia, another girl who worked in the office. She explained the rules to Sylvia and then offered her the gambit, 'What would be the first thing you'd do?' Sylvia had not shown the decency of even a second of hesitation. 'Well,' she said, 'the first thing I'd do, I'd go out and hire somebody to shoot Mrs Gary Cooper, and then . . . ' So it is to be seen that she was no fun.

But Annabel and Midge were surely born to be comrades, for Midge played the game like a master from the moment she learned it. It was she who added the touches that made the whole thing cosier. According to Midge's innovations, the eccentric who died and left you the money was not anybody you loved, or, for the matter of that, anybody you even knew. It was somebody who had seen you somewhere and had thought, 'That girl ought to have lots of nice things. I'm going to leave her a million dollars when I die.' And the death was to be neither untimely nor painful. Your benefactor, full of years and comfortably ready to depart, was to slip softly away during sleep and go right to heaven. These embroideries permitted Annabel and Midge to play their game in the luxury of peaceful consciences.

Midge played with a seriousness that was not only proper but extreme. The single strain on the girls' friendship had followed an announcement once made by Annabel that the first thing she would buy with her million dollars would be a silver-fox coat. It was as if she had struck Midge across the mouth. When Midge recovered her breath, she cried that she couldn't imagine how Annabel could do such a thing – silver-fox coats were common! Annabel defended her taste with the retort that they were not common, either. Midge then said that they were so. She added that everybody had a silver-fox coat. She went on, with perhaps a slight loss of head, to declare that she herself wouldn't be caught dead in silver fox.

For the next few days, though the girls saw each other as constantly, their conversation was careful and infrequent, and they did not once play their game. Then one morning, as soon as Annabel entered the office, she came to Midge and said that she had changed her mind. She would not buy a silver-fox coat with any part of her million dollars. Immediately on receiving the legacy, she would select a coat of mink.

Midge smiled and her eyes shone. 'I think', she said, 'you're doing absolutely the right thing.'

Now, as they walked along Fifth Avenue, they played the game anew. It was one of those days with which September is repeatedly cursed; hot and glaring, with slivers of dust in the wind. People drooped and shambled, but the girls carried themselves tall and walked a straight line, as befitted young heiresses on their afternoon promenade. There was no longer need for them to start the game at its formal opening. Annabel went direct to the heart of it.

'All right,' she said. 'So you've got this million dollars. So what would be the first thing you'd do?'

'Well, the first thing I'd do,' Midge said, 'I'd get a mink coat.' But she said it mechanically, as if she were giving the memorised answer to an expected question.

'Yes,' Annabel said, 'I think you ought to. The terribly dark kind of mink.' But she, too, spoke as if by rote. It was too hot; fur, no matter how dark and sleek and supple, was horrid to the thoughts.

They stepped along in silence for a while. Then Midge's eye was caught by a shop window. Cool, lovely gleamings were there set off by chaste and elegant darkness.

'No,' Midge said, 'I take it back. I wouldn't get a mink coat the first thing. Know what I'd do? I'd get a string of pearls. Real pearls.'

Annabel's eyes turned to follow Midge's.

'Yes,' she said, slowly. 'I think that's a kind of a good idea. And it would make sense, too. Because you can wear pearls with anything.'

Together they went over to the shop window and stood pressed against it. It contained but one object – a double row of great, even pearls clasped by a deep emerald around a little pink velvet throat.

'What do you suppose they cost?' Annabel said.

'Gee, I don't know,' Midge said. 'Plenty, I guess.'

'Like a thousand dollars?' Annabel said.

'Oh, I guess like more,' Midge said. 'On account of the emerald.'

'Well, like ten thousand dollars?' Annabel said.

'Gee, I wouldn't even know,' Midge said.

The devil nudged Annabel in the ribs. 'Dare you to go in and price them,' she said.

'Like fun!' Midge said.

'Dare you,' Annabel said.

'Why, a store like this wouldn't even be open this afternoon,' Midge said.

'Yes, it is so, too,' Annabel said. 'People just came out. And there's a doorman on. Dare you.'

'Well,' Midge said. 'But you've got to come too.'

They tendered thanks, icily, to the doorman for ushering them into the shop. It was cool and quiet, a broad, gracious room with panelled walls and soft carpet. But the girls wore expressions of bitter disdain, as if they stood in a sty.

A slim, immaculate clerk came to them and bowed. His neat face showed no astonishment at their appearance.

'Good afternoon,' he said. He implied that he would never forget it if they would grant him the favour of accepting his soft-spoken greeting.

'Good afternoon,' Annabel and Midge said together, and in like freezing accents.

'Is there something—?' the clerk said.

'Oh, we're just looking,' Annabel said. It was as if she flung the words down from a dais.

The clerk bowed.

'My friend and myself merely happened to be passing,' Midge said, and stopped, seeming to listen to the phrase. 'My friend here and myself', she went on, 'merely happened to be wondering how much are those pearls you've got in your window.'

'Ah, yes,' the clerk said. 'The double rope. That is two hundred and fifty thousand dollars, madam.'

'I see,' Midge said.

The clerk bowed. 'An exceptionally beautiful necklace,' he said. 'Would you care to look at it?'

'No thank you,' Annabel said.

'My friend and myself merely happened to be passing,' Midge said.

They turned to go; to go, from their manner, where the tumbrel awaited them. The clerk sprang ahead and opened the door. He bowed as they swept by him.

The girls went on along the Avenue and disdain was still on their faces.

'Honestly!' Annabel said. 'Can you imagine a thing like that?'

'Two hundred and fifty thousand dollars!' Midge said. 'That's a quarter of a million dollars right there!'

'He's got his nerve!' Annabel said.

They walked on. Slowly the disdain went, slowly and completely as if drained from them, and with it went the regal carriage and tread. Their shoulders dropped and they dragged their feet; they bumped against each other, without notice or apology, and caromed away again. They were silent and their eyes were cloudy.

Suddenly Midge straightened her back, flung her head high, and spoke, clear and strong.

'Listen, Annabel,' she said. 'Look. Suppose there was this terribly rich person, see? You don't know this person, but this person has seen you somewhere and wants to do something for you. Well, it's a terribly old person, see? And so this person dies, just like going to sleep, and leaves you ten million dollars. Now, what would be the first thing you'd do?'

Now at Liberty

Little white love, your way you've taken;
  Now I am left alone, alone.
Little white love, my heart's forsaken.
  (Whom shall I get by telephone?)
Well do I know there's no returning;
  Once you go out, it's done, it's done.
All of my days are grey with yearning.
  (Nevertheless, a girl needs fun.)

Little white love, perplexed and weary,
  Sadly your banner fluttered down.
Sullen the days, and dreary, dreary.
  (Which of the boys is still in town?)
Radiant and sure, you came a-flying;
  Puzzled, you left on lagging feet.
Slow in my breast, my heart is dying.
  (Nevertheless, a girl must eat.)

Little white love, I hailed you gladly;
  Now I must wave you out of sight.
Ah, but you used me badly, badly.
  (Who'd like to take me out tonight?)
All of the blundering words I've spoken,
  Little white love, forgive, forgive.
Once you went out, my heart fell, broken.
  (Nevertheless, a girl must live.)

Portrait of the Artist

Oh, lead me to a quiet cell
   Where never footfall rankles,
And bar the window passing well,
   And gyve my wrists and ankles.

Oh, wrap my eyes with linen fair,
   With hempen cord go bind me,
And, of your mercy, leave me there,
   Nor tell them where to find me.

Oh, lock the portal as you go,
   And see its bolts be double . . .
Come back in half an hour or so,
   And I will be in trouble.

Reuben's Children

Accursed from their birth they be
Who seek to find monogamy,
Pursuing it from bed to bed –
I think they would be better dead.

Ballade of a Great Weariness

There's little to have but the things I had,
  There's little to bear but the things I bore.
There's nothing to carry and naught to add,
  And glory to Heaven, I paid the score.
There's little to do but I did before,
  There's little to learn but the things I know;
And this is the sum of a lasting lore:
  Scratch a lover, and find a foe.

And couldn't it be I was young and mad
  If ever my heart on my sleeve I wore?
There's many to claw at a heart unclad,
  And little the wonder it ripped and tore.
There's one that'll join in their push and roar,
  With stories to jabber, and stones to throw;
He'll fetch you a lesson that costs you sore –
  Scratch a lover, and find a foe.

So little I'll offer to you, my lad;
  It's little in loving I set my store.
There's many a maid would be flushed and glad,
  And better you'll knock at a kindlier door.
I'll dig at my lettuce, and sweep my floor –
  Forever, forever I'm done with woe –
And happen I'll whistle about my chore,
  'Scratch a lover, and find a foe.'

L'envoi

Oh, beggar or prince, no more, no more!
  Be off and away with your strut and show.
The sweeter the apple, the blacker the core –
  Scratch a lover, and find a foe!

A TELEPHONE CALL

Please, God, let him telephone me now. Dear God, let him call me now. I won't ask anything else of You, truly I won't. It isn't very much to ask. It would be so little to You, God, such a little, little thing. Only let him telephone now. Please, God. Please, please, please.

If I didn't think about it, maybe the telephone might ring. Sometimes it does that. If I could think of something else. If I could think of something else. Maybe if I counted five hundred by fives, it might ring by that time. I'll count slowly. I won't cheat. And if it rings when I get to three hundred, I won't stop; I won't answer it until I get to five hundred. Five, ten, fifteen, twenty, twenty-five, thirty, thirty-five, forty, forty-five, fifty . . . Oh, please ring. Please.

This is the last time I'll look at the clock. I will not look at it again. It's ten minutes past seven. He said he would telephone at five o'clock. 'I'll call you at five, darling.' I think that's where he said 'darling'. I'm almost sure he said it there. I know he called me 'darling' twice, and the other time was when he said goodbye. 'Goodbye, darling.' He was busy, and he can't say much in the office, but he called me 'darling' twice. He couldn't have minded my calling him up. I know you shouldn't keep telephoning them – I know they don't like that. When you do that, they know you are thinking about them and wanting them, and that makes them hate you. But I hadn't talked to him in three days – not in three days. And all I did was ask him how he was; it was just the way anybody might have called him up. He couldn't have minded that. He couldn't have thought I was bothering him. 'No, of course you're not,' he said. And he said he'd telephone me. He didn't have to say that. I didn't ask him to, truly I didn't. I'm sure I didn't. I don't think he would say he'd telephone me, and then just never do it. Please don't let him do that, God. Please don't.

'I'll call you at five, darling.' 'Goodbye, darling.' He was busy, and he was in a hurry, and there were people around him, but he called me 'darling' twice. That's mine, that's mine. I have

that, even if I never see him again. Oh, but that's so little. That isn't enough. Nothing's enough, if I never see him again. Please let me see him again, God. Please, I want him so much. I want him so much. I'll be good, God. I will try to be better, I will, if You will let me see him again. If You will let him telephone me. Oh, let him telephone me now.

Ah, don't let my prayer seem too little to You, God. You sit up there, so white and old, with all the angels about You and the stars slipping by. And I come to You with a prayer about a telephone call. Ah, don't laugh, God. You see, You don't know how it feels. You're so safe, there on Your throne, with the blue swirling under You. Nothing can touch You; no one can twist Your heart in his hands. This is suffering, God, this is bad, bad suffering. Won't You help me? For Your Son's sake, help me. You said You would do whatever was asked of You in His name. Oh, God, in the name of Thine only beloved Son, Jesus Christ, our Lord, let him telephone me now.

I must stop this. I mustn't be this way. Look. Suppose a young man says he'll call a girl up, and then something happens, and he doesn't. That isn't so terrible, is it? Why, it's going on all over the world, right this minute. Oh, what do I care what's going on all over the world? Why can't that telephone ring? Why can't it, why can't it? Couldn't you ring? Ah, please, couldn't you? You damned, ugly, shiny thing. It would hurt you to ring, wouldn't it? Oh, that would hurt you. Damn you, I'll pull your filthy roots out of the wall, I'll smash your smug black face in little bits. Damn you to hell.

No, no, no. I must stop. I must think about something else. This is what I'll do. I'll put the clock in the other room. Then I can't look at it. If I do have to look at it, then I'll have to walk into the bedroom, and that will be something to do. Maybe, before I look at it again, he will call me. I'll be so sweet to him, if he calls me. If he says he can't see me tonight, I'll say, 'Why, that's all right, dear. Why, of course it's all right.' I'll be the way I was when I first met him. Then maybe he'll like me again. I was always sweet, at first. Oh, it's so easy to be sweet to people before you love them.

I think he must still like me a little. He couldn't have called me 'darling' twice today, if he didn't still like me a little. It isn't all gone, if he still likes me a little; even if it's only a little, little bit. You see, God, if You would just let him telephone me, I wouldn't have to ask You anything more. I would be sweet to him, I would be gay, I would be just the way I used to be, and then he would love me again. And then I would never have to ask You for anything more. Don't You see, God? So won't You please let him telephone me? Won't You please, please, please?

Are You punishing me, God, because I've been bad? Are You angry with me because I did that? Oh, but, God, there are so many bad people – You could not be hard only to me. And it wasn't very bad; it couldn't have been bad. We didn't hurt anybody, God. Things are only bad when they hurt people. We didn't hurt one single soul; You know that. You know it wasn't bad, don't You, God? So won't You let him telephone me now?

If he doesn't telephone me, I'll know God is angry with me. I'll count five hundred by fives, and if he hasn't called me then, I will know God isn't going to help me, ever again. That will be the sign. Five, ten, fifteen, twenty, twenty-five, thirty, thirty-five, forty, forty-five, fifty, fifty-five . . . It was bad. I knew it was bad. All right, God, send me to hell. You think You're frightening me with Your hell, don't You? You think Your hell is worse than mine.

I mustn't. I mustn't do this. Suppose he's a little late calling me up – that's nothing to get hysterical about. Maybe he isn't going to call – maybe he's coming straight up here without telephoning. He'll be cross if he sees I have been crying. They don't like you to cry. He doesn't cry. I wish to God I could make him cry. I wish I could make him cry and tread the floor and feel his heart heavy and big and festering in him. I wish I could hurt him like hell.

He doesn't wish that about me. I don't think he even knows how he makes me feel. I wish he could know, without my telling him. They don't like you to tell them they've made you cry. They don't like you to tell them you're unhappy because of them. If you do, they think you're possessive and exacting. And then they hate you. They hate you whenever you say anything you really think. You always have to keep playing little games. Oh, I thought we didn't have to; I thought this was so big I could say whatever I meant. I guess you can't, ever. I guess there isn't ever anything big enough for that. Oh, if he would just telephone, I wouldn't tell him I had been sad about him. They hate sad people. I would be so sweet and so gay, he couldn't help but like me. If he would only telephone. If he would only telephone.

Maybe that's what he is doing. Maybe he is coming on here without calling me up. Maybe he's on his way now. Something might have happened to him. No, nothing could ever happen to him. I can't picture anything happening to him. I never picture him run over. I never see him lying still and long and dead. I wish he were dead. That's a terrible wish. That's a lovely wish. If he were dead, he would be mine. If he were dead, I would never think of now and the last few weeks. I would remember only the lovely times. It would be all beautiful. I wish he were dead. I wish he were dead, dead, dead.

This is silly. It's silly to go wishing people were dead just because they don't call you up the very minute they said they would. Maybe the clock's fast; I don't know whether it's right. Maybe he's hardly late at all. Anything could have made him a little late. Maybe he had to stay at his office. Maybe he went home, to call me up from there, and somebody came in. He doesn't like to telephone me in front of people. Maybe he's worried, just a little, little bit, about keeping me waiting. He might even hope that I would call him up. I could do that. I could telephone him.

I mustn't. I mustn't, I mustn't. Oh, God, please don't let me telephone him. Please keep me from doing that. I know, God, just as well as You do, that if he were worried about me, he'd telephone no matter where he was or how many people there were around him. Please make me know that, God. I don't ask You to make it easy for me – You can't do that, for all that You could make a world. Only let me know it, God. Don't let me go on hoping. Don't let me say comforting things to myself. Please don't let me hope, dear God. Please don't.

I won't telephone him. I'll never telephone him again as long as I live. He'll rot in hell, before I'll call him up. You don't have to give me strength, God; I have it myself. If he wanted me, he could get me. He knows where I am. He knows I'm waiting here. He's so sure of me, so sure. I wonder why they hate you, as soon as they are sure of you. I should think it would be so sweet to be sure.

It would be so easy to telephone him. Then I'd know. Maybe it wouldn't be a foolish thing to do. Maybe he wouldn't mind. Maybe he'd like it. Maybe he has been trying to get me. Sometimes people try and try to get you on the telephone, and they say the number doesn't answer. I'm not just saying that to help myself; that really happens. You know that really happens, God. Oh, God, keep me away from the telephone. Keep me away. Let me still have just a little bit of pride. I think I'm going to need it, God. I think it will be all I'll have.

Oh, what does pride matter, when I can't stand it if I don't talk to him? Pride like that is such a silly, shabby little thing. The real pride, the big pride, is in having no pride. I'm not saying that just because I want to call him. I am not. That's true, I know that's true. I will be big. I will be beyond little prides.

Please, God, keep me from telephoning him. Please, God.

I don't see what pride has to do with it. This is such a little thing, for me to be bringing in pride, for me to be making such a fuss about. I may have misunderstood him. Maybe he said for me to call him up, at five. 'Call me at five, darling.' He could have said that, perfectly well. It's so possible that I didn't hear him right. 'Call me at five, darling.' I'm almost sure that's what he said. God, don't let me talk this way to myself. Make me know, please make me know.

I'll think about something else. I'll just sit quietly. If I could sit still. If I could sit still. Maybe I could read. Oh, all the books are about people who love each other, truly and sweetly. What do they want to write about that for? Don't they know it isn't true? Don't they know it's a lie, it's a god-damned lie? What do they have to tell about that for, when they know how it hurts? Damn them, damn them, damn them.

I won't. I'll be quiet. This is nothing to get excited about. Look. Suppose he were someone I didn't know very well. Suppose he were another girl. Then I'd just telephone and say, 'Well, for goodness' sake, what happened to you?' That's what I'd do, and I'd never even think about it. Why can't I be casual and natural, just because I love him? I can be. Honestly, I can be. I'll call him up, and be so easy and pleasant. You see if I won't, God. Oh, don't let me call him. Don't, don't, don't.

God, aren't You really going to let him call me? Are You sure, God? Couldn't You please relent? Couldn't You? I don't even ask You to let him telephone me this minute, God; only let him do it in a little while. I'll count five hundred by fives. I'll do it so slowly and so fairly. If he hasn't telephoned then, I'll call him. I will. Oh, please, dear God, dear kind God, my blessed Father in Heaven, let him call before then. Please, God. Please.

Five, ten, fifteen, twenty, twenty-five, thirty, thirty-five . . .

Plea

Secrets, you said, would hold us two apart;
You'd have me know of you your least transgression,
And so the intimate places of your heart,
Kneeling, you bared to me, as in confession.
Softly you told of loves that went before –
Of clinging arms, of kisses gladly given;
Luxuriously clean of heart once more,
You rose up, then, and stood before me, shriven.

When this, my day of happiness, is through,
And love, that bloomed so fair, turns brown and brittle,
There is a thing that I shall ask of you –
I, who have given so much, and asked so little.
Some day, when there's another in my stead,
Again you'll feel the need of absolution,
And you will go to her, and bow your head,
And offer her your past, as contribution.

When with your list of loves you overcome her,
For Heaven's sake, keep this one secret from her!

Love Song

My own dear love, he is strong and bold
And he cares not what comes after.
His words ring sweet as a chime of gold,
And his eyes are lit with laughter.
He is jubilant as a flag unfurled –
Oh, a girl, she'd not forget him.
My own dear love, he is all my world –
And I wish I'd never met him.

My love, he's mad, and my love, he's fleet,
And a wild young wood-thing bore him!
The ways are fair to his roaming feet,
And the skies are sunlit for him.
As sharply sweet to my heart he seems
As the fragrance of acacia.
My own dear love, he is all my dreams –
And I wish he were in Asia.

My love runs by like a day in June,
And he makes no friends of sorrows.
He'll tread his galloping rigadoon
In the pathway of the morrows.
He'll live his days where the sunbeams start,
Nor could storm or wind uproot him.
My own dear love, he is all my heart –
And I wish somebody'd shoot him.

Interview

The ladies men admire, I've heard,
Would shudder at a wicked word.
Their candle gives a single light;
They'd rather stay at home at night.
They do not keep awake till three,
Nor read erotic poetry.
They never sanction the impure,
Nor recognise an overture.
They shrink from powders and from paints . . .
So far, I have had no complaints.

The Burned Child

Love has had his way with me.
  This my heart is torn and maimed
Since he took his play with me.
  Cruel well the bow-boy aimed,

Shot, and saw the feathered shaft
  Dripping bright and bitter red.
He that shrugged his wings and laughed –
  Better had he left me dead.

Sweet, why do you plead me, then,
  Who have bled so sore of that?
Could I bear it once again? . . .
  Drop a hat, dear, drop a hat!

HERE WE ARE

The young man in the new blue suit finished arranging the glistening luggage in tight corners of the Pullman compartment. The train had leaped at curves and bounced along straightaways, rendering balance a praiseworthy achievement and a sporadic one; and the young man had pushed and hoisted and tucked and shifted the bags with concentrated care.

Nevertheless, eight minutes for the settling of two suitcases and a hat-box is a long time.

He sat down, leaning back against bristled green plush, in the seat opposite the girl in beige. She looked as new as a peeled egg. Her hat, her fur, her frock, her gloves were glossy and stiff with novelty. On the arc of the thin, slippery sole of one beige shoe was gummed a tiny oblong of white paper, printed with the price set and paid for that slipper and its fellow, and the name of the shop that had dispensed them.

She had been staring raptly out of the window, drinking in the big weathered signboards that extolled the phenomena of codfish without bones and screens no rust could corrupt. As the young man sat down, she turned politely from the pane, met his eyes, started a smile and got it about half done, and rested her gaze just above his right shoulder.

'Well!' the young man said.

'Well!' she said.

'Well, here we are,' he said.

'Here we are,' she said. 'Aren't we?'

'I should say we were,' he said. 'Eeyop. Here we are.'

'Well!' she said.

'Well!' he said. 'Well. How does it feel to be an old married lady?'

'Oh, it's too soon to ask me that,' she said. 'At least – I mean. Well, I mean, goodness, we've only been married about three hours, haven't we?'

The young man studied his wrist-watch as if he were just acquiring the knack of reading time.

'We have been married', he said, 'exactly two hours and twenty-six minutes.'

'My,' she said. 'It seems like longer.'

'No,' he said. 'It isn't hardly half-past six yet.'

'It seems like later,' she said. 'I guess it's because it starts getting dark so early.'

'It does, at that,' he said. 'The nights are going to be pretty long from now on. I mean. I mean – well, it starts getting dark early.'

'I didn't have any idea what time it was,' she said. 'Everything was so mixed up, I sort of don't know where I am, or what it's all about. Getting back from the church, and then all those people, and then changing all my clothes, and then everybody throwing things, and all. Goodness, I don't see how people do it every day.'

'Do what?' he said.

'Get married,' she said. 'When you think of all the people, all over the world, getting married just as if it was nothing. Chinese people and everybody. Just as if it wasn't anything.'

'Well, let's not worry about people all over the world,' he said. 'Let's don't think about a lot of Chinese. We've got something better to think about. I mean. I mean – well, what do we care about them?'

'I know,' she said. 'But I just sort of got to thinking of them, all of them, all over everywhere, doing it all the time. At least, I mean – getting married, you know. And it's – well, it's sort of such a big thing to do, it makes you feel queer. You think of them, all of them, all doing it just like it wasn't anything. And how does anybody know what's going to happen next?'

'Let them worry,' he said. 'We don't have to. We know darn well what's going to happen next. I mean. I mean – well, we know it's going to be great. Well, we know we're going to be happy. Don't we?'

'Oh, of course,' she said. 'Only you think of all the people, and you have to sort of keep thinking. It makes you feel funny. An awful lot of people that get married, it doesn't turn out so well. And I guess they all must have thought it was going to be great.'

'Come on, now,' he said. 'This is no way to start a honeymoon, with all this thinking going on. Look at us – all married and everything done. I mean. The wedding all done and all.'

'Ah, it was nice, wasn't it?' she said. 'Did you really like my veil?'

'You looked great,' he said. 'Just great.'

'Oh, I'm terribly glad,' she said. 'Ellie and Louise looked lovely, didn't they? I'm terribly glad they did finally decide on pink. They looked perfectly lovely.'

'Listen,' he said. 'I want to tell you something. When I was standing up there in that old church waiting for you to come up, and I saw those two bridesmaids, I thought to myself, I thought, "Well, I never knew Louise could look like that!" Why, she'd have knocked anybody's eye out.'

'Oh, really?' she said. 'Funny. Of course, everybody thought her dress and hat were lovely, but a lot of people seemed to think she looked sort of tired. People have been saying that a lot, lately. I tell them I think it's awfully mean of them to go around saying that about her. I tell them they've got to remember that Louise isn't so terribly young any more, and they've got to expect her to look like that. Louise can say she's twenty-three all she wants to, but she's a good deal nearer twenty-seven.'

'Well, she was certainly a knock-out at the wedding,' he said. 'Boy!'

'I'm terribly glad you thought so,' she said. 'I'm glad someone did. How did you think Ellie looked?'

'Why, I honestly didn't get a look at her,' he said.

'Oh, really?' she said. 'Well, I certainly think that's too bad. I don't suppose I ought to say it about my own sister, but I never saw anybody look as beautiful as Ellie looked today. And always so sweet and unselfish, too. And you didn't even notice her. But you never pay attention to Ellie, anyway. Don't think I haven't noticed it. It makes me feel just terrible. It makes me feel just awful, that you don't like my own sister.'

'I do so like her!' he said. 'I'm crazy for Ellie. I think she's a great kid.'

'Don't think it makes any difference to Ellie!' she said.

'Ellie's got enough people crazy about her. It isn't anything to her whether you like her or not. Don't flatter yourself she cares! Only, the only thing is, it makes it awfully hard for me you don't like her, that's the only thing. I keep thinking, when we come back and get in the apartment and everything, it's going to be awfully hard for me that you won't want my own sister to come and see me. It's going to make it awfully hard for me that you won't ever want my family around. I know how you feel about my family. Don't think I haven't seen it. Only, if you don't ever want to see them, that's your loss. Not theirs. Don't flatter yourself!'

'Oh now, come on!' he said. 'What's all this talk about not wanting your family around? Why, you know how I feel about your family. I think your old lady – I think your mother's swell. And Ellie. And your father. What's all this talk?'

'Well, I've seen it,' she said. 'Don't think I haven't. Lots of people they get married, and they think it's going to be great and everything, and then it all goes to pieces because people don't like people's families, or something like that. Don't tell me! I've seen it happen.'

'Honey,' he said 'what is all this? What are you getting all angry about? Hey, look, this is our honeymoon. What are you trying to start a fight for? Ah, I guess you're just feeling sort of nervous.'

'Me?' she said. 'What have I got to be nervous about? I mean. I mean, goodness, I'm not nervous.'

'You know, lots of times', he said, 'they say that girls get kind of nervous and yippy on account of thinking about – I mean. I mean – well, it's like you said, things are all so sort of mixed up and everything, right now. But afterwards, it'll be all right. I mean. I mean – well, look, honey, you don't look any too comfortable. Don't you want to take your hat off? And let's don't ever fight, ever. Will we?'

'Ah, I'm sorry I was cross,' she said. 'I guess I did feel a little bit funny. All mixed up, and then thinking of all those people all over everywhere, and then being sort of 'way off here, all alone with you. It's so sort of different. It's sort of such a big thing. You can't blame a person for thinking, can you? Yes, don't let's ever, ever fight. We won't be like a whole lot of them. We won't fight or be nasty or anything. Will we?'

'You bet your life we won't,' he said.

'I guess I will take this darned old hat off,' she said. 'It kind of presses. Just put it up on the rack, will you, dear? Do you like it, sweetheart?'

'Looks good on you,' he said.

'No, but I mean', she said, 'do you really like it?'

'Well, I'll tell you,' he said. 'I know this is the new style and everything like that, and it's probably great. I don't know anything about things like that. Only I like the kind of a hat like that blue hat you had. Gee, I liked that hat.'

'Oh, really?' she said. 'Well, that's nice. That's lovely. The first thing you say to me, as soon as you get me off on a train away from my family and everything, is that you don't like my hat. The first thing you say to your wife is you think she has terrible taste in hats. That's nice, isn't it?'

'Now, honey,' he said, 'I never said anything like that. I only said — '

'What you don't seem to realise', she said, 'is this hat cost twenty-two dollars. Twenty-two dollars. And that horrible old blue thing you think you're so crazy about, that cost three ninety-five.'

'I don't give a darn what they cost,' he said. 'I only said – I said I liked that blue hat. I don't know anything about hats. I'll be crazy about this one as soon as I get used to it. Only it's kind of not like your other hats. I don't know about the new styles. What do I know about women's hats?'

'It's too bad', she said, 'you didn't marry somebody that would get the kind of hats you'd like. Hats that cost three ninety-five. Why didn't you marry Louise? You always think she looks so beautiful. You'd love her taste in hats. Why didn't you marry her?'

'Ah, now, honey,' he said. 'For Heaven's sakes!'

'Why didn't you marry her?' she said. 'All you've done, ever since we got on this train, is talk about her. Here I've sat and sat, and just listened to you saying how wonderful Louise is. I suppose that's nice, getting me all off here alone with you, and then raving about Louise right in front of my face. Why didn't you ask her to marry you? I'm sure she would have jumped at the chance. There aren't so many people asking her to marry them. It's too bad you didn't marry her. I'm sure you'd have been much happier.'

'Listen, baby,' he said, 'while you're talking about things like that, why didn't you marry Joe Brooks? I suppose he could have given you all the twenty-two-dollar hats you wanted, I suppose!'

'Well, I'm not so sure I'm not sorry I didn't,' she said. 'There! Joe Brooks wouldn't have waited until he got me all off alone and then sneered at my taste in clothes. Joe Brooks wouldn't ever hurt my feelings. Joe Brooks has always been fond of me. There!'

'Yeah,' he said. 'He's fond of you. He was so fond of you he didn't even send a wedding present. That's how fond of you he was.'

'I happen to know for a fact', she said, 'that he was away on business, and as soon as he comes back he's going to give me anything I want for the apartment.'

'Listen,' he said. 'I don't want anything he gives you in our apartment. Anything he gives you, I'll throw right out the window. That's what I think of your friend Joe Brooks. And how do you know where he is and what he's going to do, anyway? Has he been writing to you?'

'I suppose my friends can correspond with me,' she said. 'I didn't hear there was any law against that.'

'Well, I suppose they can't!' he said. 'And what do you think of that? I'm not going to have my wife getting a lot of letters from cheap travelling salesmen!'

'Joe Brooks is not a cheap travelling salesman!' she said. 'He is not! He gets a wonderful salary.'

'Oh, yeah?' he said. 'Where did you hear that?'

'He told me so himself,' she said.

'Oh, he told you so himself,' he said. 'I see. He told you so himself.'

'You've got a lot of right to talk about Joe Brooks,' she said. 'You and your friend Louise. All you ever talk about is Louise.'

'Oh, for Heaven's sakes!' he said. 'What do I care about Louise? I just thought she was a friend of yours, that's all. That's why I ever even noticed her.'

'Well, you certainly took an awful lot of notice of her today,' she said. 'On our wedding day! You said yourself when you were standing there in the church you just kept thinking of her. Right up at the altar. Oh, right in the presence of God! And all you thought about was Louise.'

'Listen, honey,' he said, 'I never should have said that. How does anybody know what kind of crazy things come into their heads when they're standing there waiting to get married? I was just telling you that because it was so kind of crazy. I thought it would make you laugh.'

'I know,' she said. 'I've been all sort of mixed up today, too. I told you that. Everything so strange and everything. And me all the time thinking about all those people all over the world, and now us here all alone, and everything. I know you get all mixed up. Only I did think, when you kept talking about how beautiful Louise looked, you did it with malice and forethought.'

'I never did anything with malice and forethought!' he said. 'I just told you that about Louise because I thought it would make you laugh.'

'Well, it didn't,' she said.

'No, I know it didn't,' he said. 'It certainly did not. Ah, baby, and we ought to be laughing, too. Hell, honey lamb, this is our honeymoon. What's the matter?'

'I don't know,' she said. 'We used to squabble a lot when we were going together and then engaged and everything, but I thought everything would be so different as soon as you were married. And now I feel so sort of strange and everything. I feel so sort of alone.'

'Well, you see, sweetheart,' he said, 'we're not really married yet. I mean. I mean – well, things will be different afterwards. Oh, hell. I mean, we haven't been married very long.'

'No,' she said.

'Well, we haven't got much longer to wait now,' he said. 'I mean – well, we'll be in New York in about twenty minutes. Then we can have dinner, and sort of see what we feel like doing. Or I mean. Is there anything special you want to do tonight?'

'What?' she said.

'What I mean to say,' he said, 'would you like to go to a show or something?'

'Why, whatever you like,' she said. 'I sort of didn't think people went to theatres and things on their – I mean, I've got a couple of letters I simply must write. Don't let me forget.'

'Oh,' he said. 'You're going to write letters tonight?'

'Well, you see,' she said. 'I've been perfectly terrible. What with all the excitement and everything. I never did thank poor old Mrs Sprague for her berry spoon, and I never did a thing about those book ends the McMasters sent. It's just too awful of me. I've got to write them this very night.'

'And when you've finished writing your letters,' he said, 'maybe I could get you a magazine or a bag of peanuts.'

'What?' she said.

'I mean,' he said, 'I wouldn't want you to be bored.'

'As if I could be bored with you!' she said. 'Silly! Aren't we married? Bored!'

'What I thought,' he said, 'I thought when we got in, we could go right up to the Biltmore and anyway leave our bags, and may be have a little dinner in the room, kind of quiet, and then do whatever we wanted. I mean. I mean – well, let's go right up there from the station.'

'Oh, yes, let's,' she said. 'I'm so glad we're going to the Biltmore. I just love it. The twice I've stayed in New York we've always stayed there, Papa and Mamma and Ellie and I, and I was crazy about it. I always sleep so well there. I go right off to sleep the minute I put my head on the pillow.'

'Oh, you do?' he said.

'At least, I mean,' she said. ''Way up high it's so quiet.'

'We might go to some show or other tomorrow night

instead of tonight,' he said. 'Don't you think that would be better?'

'Yes, I think it might,' she said.

He rose, balanced a moment, crossed over and sat down beside her.

'Do you really have to write those letters tonight?' he said.

'Well,' she said, 'I don't suppose they'd get there any quicker than if I wrote them tomorrow.'

There was a silence with things going on in it.

'And we won't ever fight any more, will we?' he said.

'Oh, no,' she said. 'Not ever! I don't know what made me do like that. It all got so sort of funny, sort of like a nightmare, the way I got thinking of all those people getting married all the time; and so many of them, everything spoils on account of fighting and everything. I got all mixed up thinking about them. Oh, I don't want to be like them. But we won't be, will we?'

'Sure we won't,' he said.

'We won't go all to pieces,' she said. 'We won't fight. It'll all be different, now we're married. It'll all be lovely. Reach me down my hat, will you, sweetheart? It's time I was putting it on. Thanks. Ah, I'm so sorry you don't like it.'

'I do so like it!' he said.

'You said you didn't,' she said. 'You said you thought it was perfectly terrible.'

'I never said any such thing,' he said. 'You're crazy.'

'All right, I may be crazy,' she said. 'Thank you very much. But that's what you said. Not that it matters – it's just a little thing. But it makes you feel pretty funny to think you've gone and married somebody that says you have perfectly terrible taste in hats. And then goes and says you're crazy, beside.'

'Now, listen here,' he said. 'Nobody said any such thing. Why, I love that hat. The more I look at it the better I like it. I think it's great.'

'That isn't what you said before,' she said.

'Honey,' he said. 'Stop it, will you? What do you want to start all this for? I love the damned hat. I mean, I love your hat. I love anything you wear. What more do you want me to say?'

'Well, I don't want you to say it like that,' she said.

'I said I think it's great,' he said. 'That's all I said.'

'Do you really?' she said. 'Do you honestly? Ah, I'm so glad. I'd hate you not to like my hat. It would be – I don't know, it would be sort of such a bad start.'

'Well, I'm crazy for it,' he said. 'Now we've got that settled, for Heaven's sakes. Ah, baby. Baby lamb. We're not going to have any bad starts. Look at us – we're on our honeymoon. Pretty soon we'll be regular old married people. I mean. I mean, in a few minutes we'll be getting in to New York, and then we'll be going to the hotel, and then everything will be all right. I mean – well, look at us! Here we are married! Here we are!'

'Yes, here we are,' she said. 'Aren't we?'

Symptom Recital

I do not like my state of mind;
I'm bitter, querulous, unkind.
I hate my legs, I hate my hands,
I do not yearn for lovelier lands.
I dread the dawn's recurrent light;
I hate to go to bed at night.
I snoot at simple, earnest folk.
I cannot take the gentlest joke.
I find no peace in paint or type.
My world is but a lot of tripe.
I'm disillusioned, empty-breasted.
For what I think, I'd be arrested.
I am not sick, I am not well.
My quondam dreams are shot to hell.
My soul is crushed, my spirit sore;
I do not like me any more.
I cavil, quarrel, grumble, grouse.
I ponder on the narrow house.
I shudder at the thought of men . . .
I'm due to fall in love again.

Sanctuary

My land is bare of chattering folk;
    The clouds are low along the ridges,
And sweet's the air with curly smoke
    From all my burning bridges.

Song of One of the Girls

Here in my heart I am Helen;
I'm Aspasia and Hero, at least.
I'm Judith, and Jael, and Madame de Staël;
I'm Salome, moon of the East.

Here in my soul I am Sappho;
Lady Hamilton am I, as well.
In me Récamier vies with Kitty O'Shea,
With Dido, and Eve, and poor Nell.

I'm of the glamorous ladies
At whose beckoning history shook.
But you are a man, and see only my pan,
So I stay at home with a book.

The Choice

He'd have given me rolling lands,
Houses of marble, and billowing farms,
Pearls, to trickle between my hands,
Smouldering rubies, to circle my arms.
You – you'd only a lilting song,
Only a melody, happy and high,
You were sudden and swift and strong –
Never a thought for another had I.

He'd have given me laces rare,
Dresses that glimmered with frosty sheen,
Shining ribbons to wrap my hair,
Horses to draw me, as fine as a queen.
You – you'd only to whistle low,
Gaily I followed wherever you led.
I took you, and I let him go –
Somebody ought to examine my head!

DIDO
SALOME
SAPPHO
HELEN

DUSK BEFORE FIREWORKS

He was a very good-looking young man indeed, shaped to be annoyed. His voice was intimate as the rustle of sheets, and he kissed easily. There was no tallying the gifts of Charvet handkerchiefs, *art moderne* ashtrays, monogrammed dressing-gowns, gold key-chains, and cigarette-cases of thin wood, inlaid with views of Parisian comfort stations, that were sent him by ladies too quickly confident, and were paid for with the money of unwitting husbands, which is acceptable any place in the world. Every woman who visited his small, square apartment promptly flamed with the desire to assume charge of its redecoration. During his tenancy, three separate ladies had achieved this ambition. Each had left behind her, for her brief monument, much too much glazed chintz.

The glare of the latest upholstery was dulled, now, in an April dusk. There was a soft blur of mauve and grey over chairs and curtains, instead of the daytime pattern of heroic-sized double poppies and small, sad elephants. (The most recent of the volunteer decorators was a lady who added interest to her ways by collecting all varieties of elephants save those alive or stuffed; her selection of the chintz had been made less for the cause of contemporary design than in the hope of keeping ever present the wistful souvenirs of her hobby and, hence, of herself. Unhappily, the poppies, those flowers for forgetfulness, turned out to be predominant in the pattern.)

The very good-looking young man was stretched in a chair that was legless and short in back. It was a strain to see in that chair any virtue save the speeding one of modernity. Certainly it was a peril to all who dealt with it; they were far from their best within its arms, and they could never have wished to be remembered as they appeared while easing into its depths or struggling out again. All, that is, save the young man. He was a long young man, broad at the shoulders and chest and narrow everywhere else, and his muscles obeyed him at the exact instant of command. He rose and lay, he moved and was still, always in beauty. Several men disliked him, but only one woman really hated him. She was his sister. She was stump-shaped, and she had straight hair.

On the sofa opposite the difficult chair there sat a young woman, slight and softly dressed. There was no more to her frock than some dull, dark silk and a little chiffon, but the recurrent bill for it demanded, in bitter black and white, a sum well on toward the second hundred. Once the very good-looking young man had said that he liked women in quiet conservative clothes, carefully made. The young woman was of those unfortunates who remember every word. This made living peculiarly trying for her when it was later demonstrated that the young man was also partial to ladies given to garments of slapdash cut, and colour like the sound of big brass instruments.

The young woman was temperately pretty in the eyes of most beholders; but there were a few, mainly hand-to-mouth people, artists and such, who could not look enough at her. Half a year before, she had been sweeter to see. Now there was tension about her mouth and unease along her brow, and her eyes looked wearied and troubled. The gentle dusk became her. The young man who shared it with her could not see these things.

She stretched her arms and laced her fingers high above her head.

'Oh, this is nice,' she said. 'It's nice being here.'

'It's nice and peaceful,' he said. 'Oh, Lord. Why can't people just be peaceful? That's little enough to ask, isn't it? Why does there have to be so much hell, all the time?'

She dropped her hands to her lap.

'There doesn't have to be at all,' she said. She had a quiet voice, and she said her words with every courtesy to each of them, as if she respected language. 'There's never any need for hell.'

'There's an awful lot of it around, sweet,' he said.

'There certainly is,' she said. 'There's just as much hell as there are hundreds of little shrill, unnecessary people. It's the second-raters that stir up hell; first-rate people wouldn't. You need never have another bit of it in your beautiful life if – if you'll pardon my pointing – you could just manage to steel yourself against that band of spitting hell-cats that is included in your somewhat overcrowded acquaintance, my lamb. Ah, but I mean it, Hobie, dear. I've been wanting to tell you for so long. But it's so rotten hard to say. If I say it, it makes me sound just like one of them – makes me seem inexpensive and jealous. Surely, you know, after all this time, I'm not like that. It's just that I worry so about you. You're so fine, you're so lovely, it nearly kills me to see you just eaten up by a lot of things like Margot Wadsworth and Mrs Holt and Evie Maynard and those. You're so much better than that. You know that's why I'm saying it. You know I haven't got a stitch of jealousy in me. Jealous! Good heavens, if I were going to be jealous, I'd be it about someone worth while, and not about any silly, stupid, idle, worthless, selfish, hysterical, vulgar, promiscuous, sex-ridden — '

'Darling!' he said.

'Well, I'm sorry,' she said. 'I guess I'm sorry. I didn't really mean to go into the subject of certain of your friends. Maybe the way they behave isn't their fault,' said she, lying in her teeth. 'After all, you can't expect them to know what it's about. Poor things, they'll never know how sweet it can be, how lovely it always is when we're alone together. It is, isn't it? Ah, Hobie, isn't it?'

The young man raised his slow lids and looked at her. He smiled with one end of his beautiful curly mouth.

'Uh-huh,' he said.

He took his eyes from hers and became busy with an ash-tray and a spent cigarette. But he still smiled.

'Ah, don't,' she said. 'You promised you'd forget about – about last Wednesday. You said you'd never remember it again. Oh, whatever made me do it! Making scenes. Having tantrums. Rushing out into the night. And then coming crawling back. Me, that wanted to show you how different a woman could be! Oh, please, please, don't let's think about it. Only tell me I wasn't as terrible as I know I was.'

'Darling,' he said, for he was often a young man of simple statements, 'you were the worst I ever saw.'

'And doesn't that come straight from Sir Hubert!' she

said. 'Oh, dear. Oh, dear, oh, dear. What can I say? "Sorry" isn't nearly enough. I'm broken. I'm in little bits. Would you mind doing something about putting me together again?'

She held out her arms to him.

The young man rose, came over to the sofa, and kissed her. He had intended a quick, good-humoured kiss, a moment's stop on a projected trip out to his little pantry to mix cocktails. But her arms clasped him so close and so gladly that he dismissed the plan. He lifted her to her feet, and did not leave her.

Presently she moved her head and hid her face above his heart.

'Listen,' she said, against cloth. 'I want to say it all now, and then never say it any more. I want to tell you that there'll never, never be anything like last Wednesday again. What we have is so much too lovely ever to cheapen. I promise, oh, I promise you, I won't ever be like – like anybody else.'

'You couldn't be, Kit,' he said.

'Ah, think that always,' she said, 'and say it sometimes. It's so sweet to hear. Will you, Hobie?'

'For your size', he said, 'you talk an awful lot.' His fingers slid to her chin and he held her face for his greater convenience.

After a while she moved again.

'Guess who I'd rather be, right this minute, than anybody in the whole world,' she said.

'Who?' he said.

'Me,' she said.

The telephone rang.

The telephone was in the young man's bedroom, standing in frequent silence on the little table by his bed. There was no door to the bedchamber; a plan which had disadvantages, too. Only a curtained archway sequestered its intimacies from those of the living-room. Another archway, also streaming chintz, gave from the bedroom upon a tiny passage, along which were ranged the bathroom and the pantry. It was only by entering either of these, closing the door behind, and turning the faucets on to the full that any second person in the apartment could avoid hearing what was being said over the telephone. The young man sometimes thought of removing to a flat of more sympathetic design.

'There's that damn telephone,' the young man said.

'Isn't it?' the young woman said. 'And wouldn't it be?'

'Let's not answer it,' he said. 'Let's let it ring.'

'No, you mustn't,' she said. 'I must be big and strong. Anyway, maybe it's only somebody that just died and left you twenty million dollars. Maybe it isn't some other woman at all. And if it is, what difference does it make? See how sweet and reasonable I am? Look at me being generous.'

'You can afford to be, sweetheart,' he said.

'I know I can,' she said. 'After all, whoever she is, she's way off on an end of a wire, and I'm right here.'

She smiled up at him. So it was nearly half a minute before he went away to the telephone.

Still smiling, the young woman stretched her head back, closed her eyes and flung her arms wide. A long sigh raised her breast. Thus she stood, then she went and settled back on the sofa. She essayed whistling softly, but the issuing sounds would not resemble the intended tune and she felt, though interested, vaguely betrayed. Then she looked about the dusk-filled room. Then she pondered her finger-nails, bringing each bent hand close to her eyes, and could find no fault. Then she smoothed her skirt along her legs and shook out the chiffon frills at her wrists. Then she spread her little handkerchief on her knee and with exquisite care traced the 'Katherine' embroidered in script across one of its corners. Then she gave it all up and did nothing but listen.

'Yes?' the young man was saying. 'Hello? Hello. I *told* you this is Mr Ogden. Well, I *am* holding the wire. I've *been* holding the wire. *You're* the one that went away. Hello? Ah, now listen – Hello? Hey. Oh, what the hell *is* this? Come back, will you? Operator! Hello, *yes*, this is Mr Ogden. Who? Oh, hello, Connie. How are you, dear? What? You're what? Oh, that's too bad. What's the matter? Why can't you? Where are you, in Greenwich? Oh, I see. When, now? Why, Connie, the only thing is I've got to go right out. So if you came into town now, it really wouldn't do much – well, I couldn't very well do that, dear. I'm keeping these people waiting as it is. I say I'm late now, I was just going out the door when you called. Why, I'd better not say that, Connie, because there's no telling when I'll be able to break away. Look, why don't you wait and come into town tomorrow sometime? What? Can't you tell me now? Oh – Well – Oh, Connie, there's no reason to talk like that. Why, of course I'd do anything in the world I could, but I tell you I can't tonight. No, no, no, no, no, it isn't that at all. No, it's nothing like that, I tell you. These people are friends of my sister's, and it's just one of those things you've got to do. Why don't you be a good girl and go to bed early, and then you'll feel better tomorrow? Hm? Will you do that? What? Of course I do, Connie. I'll try to later on if I can, dear. Well, all right, if you want to, but I don't know what time I'll be home. Of course I do. Of course I do. Yes, *do*, Connie. You be a good girl, won't you? 'Bye, dear.'

The young man returned, through the chintz. He had a rather worn look. It was, of course, becoming to him.

'God,' he said, simply.

The young woman on the sofa looked at him as if through clear ice.

'And how *is* dear Mrs Holt?' she said.

'Great,' he said. 'Corking. Way up at the top of her form.' He dropped wearily into the low chair. 'She says she has something she wants to tell me.'

'It can't be her age,' she said.

He smiled without joy. 'She says it's too hard to say over the wire,' he said.

'Then it may be her age,' she said. 'She's afraid it might sound like her telephone number.'

'About twice a week', he said, 'Connie has something she must tell you right away, that she couldn't possibly say over the telephone. Usually it turns out she's caught the butler drinking again.'

'I see,' she said.

'Well,' he said. 'Poor little Connie.'

'Poor little Connie,' she said. 'Oh, my God. That sabre-toothed tigress. Poor little Connie.'

'Darling, why do we have to waste time talking about Connie Holt?' he said. 'Can't we just be peaceful?'

'Not while that she-beast prowls the streets,' she said. 'Is she coming into town tonight?'

'Well, she was,' he said, 'but then she more or less said she wouldn't.'

'Oh, she will,' she said. 'You get right down out of that fool's paradise you're in. She'll shoot out of Greenwich like a bat out of hell, if she thinks there's a chance of seeing you. Ah, Hobie, you don't really want to see that old thing, do you? Do you? Because if you do – Well, I suppose maybe you do. Naturally, if she has something she must tell you right away, you want to see her. Look, Hobie, you know you can see me any time. It isn't a bit important, seeing me tonight. Why don't you call up Mrs Holt and tell her to take the next train in? She'd get here quicker by train than by motor, wouldn't she? Please go ahead and do it. It's quite all right about me. Really.'

'You know,' he said, 'I knew that was coming. I could tell it by the way you were when I came back from the telephone. Oh, Kit, what makes you want to talk like that? You know damned well the last thing I want to do is see Connie Holt. You know how I want to be with you. Why do you want to work up all this? I watched you just sit there and deliberately talk yourself into it, starting right out of nothing. Now what's the idea of that? Oh, good Lord, what's the matter with women, anyway?'

'Please don't call me "women",' she said.

'I'm sorry, darling,' he said. 'I didn't mean to use bad words.' He smiled at her. She felt her heart go liquid, but she did her best to be harder won.

'Doubtless', she said, and her words fell like snow when there is no wind, 'I spoke ill-advisedly. If I said, as I must have, something to distress you, I can only beg you to believe that that was my misfortune, and not my intention. It seemed to me as if I were doing only a courteous thing in suggesting that you need feel no obligation about spending the evening with me, when you would naturally wish to be with Mrs Holt. I simply felt that – Oh, the hell with it! I'm no good at this. Of course I didn't mean it, dearest. If you had said, "All right", and had gone and told her to come in, I should have died. I just said it because I wanted to hear you say it was me you wanted to be with. Oh, I need to hear you say that, Hobie. It's – it's what I live on, darling.'

'Kit,' he said, 'you ought to know, without my saying it. You know. It's this feeling you *have* to say things – that's what spoils everything.'

'I suppose so,' she said. 'I suppose I know so. Only – the thing is, I get so mixed up, I just – I just can't go on. I've got to be reassured, dearest. I didn't need to be at first, when everything was gay and sure, but things aren't – well, they aren't the same now. There seem to be so many others that – So I need so terribly to have you tell me that it's me and not anybody else. Oh, I *had* to have you say that, a few minutes ago. Look, Hobie. How do you think it makes me feel to sit here and hear you lie to Connie Holt – to hear you say you have to go out with friends of your sister's? Now why couldn't you say you had a date with me? Are you ashamed of me, Hobie? Is it that?'

'O Kit,' he said, 'for Heaven's sake! I don't know why I did it. I did it before I even thought. I did it – well, sort of instinctively, I guess, because it seemed to be the easiest thing to do. I suppose I'm just weak.'

'No!' she said. 'You weak? Well! And is there any other news tonight?'

'I know I am,' he said. 'I know it's weak to do anything in the world to avoid a scene.'

'Exactly what', she said, 'is Mrs Holt to you and you to her that she may make a scene if she learns that you have an engagement with another woman?'

'O God!' he said. 'I told you I don't give a damn about Connie Holt. She's nothing to me. Now will you for God's sake let it drop?'

'Oh, she's nothing to you,' she said. 'I see. Naturally, that would be why you called her "dear" every other word.'

'If I did,' he said, 'I never knew I was saying it. Good Lord, that doesn't mean anything. It's simply a – a form of nervousness, I suppose. I say it when I can't think what to call people. Why, I call telephone operators "dear".'

'I'm sure you do!' she said.

They glared. It was the young man who gave first. He went and sat close to her on the sofa, and for a while there were only murmurs. Then he said, 'Will you stop? Will you stop it? Will you always be just like this – just sweet and the way you're meant to be and no fighting?'

'I will,' she said. 'Honest, I mean to. Let's not let anything come between us again ever. Mrs Holt, indeed! Hell with her.'

'Hell with her,' he said. There was another silence, during which the young man did several things that he did extraordinarily well.

Suddenly the young woman stiffened her arms and pushed him away from her.

'And how do I know', she said, 'that the way you talk to me about Connie Holt isn't just the way you talk to her about me when I'm not here? How do I know that?'

'O my Lord,' he said. 'O my dear, sweet Lord. Just when everything was all right. Ah, stop it, will you, baby? Let's just be quiet. Like this. See?'

A little later he said, 'Look, sweet, how about a cocktail? Mightn't that be an idea? I'll go make them. And would you like the lights lighted?'

'Oh, no,' she said. 'I like it better in the dusk, like this. It's sweet. Dusk is so personal, somehow. And this way you can't see those lampshades. Hobie, if you knew how I hate your lampshades!'

'Honestly?' he said, with less injury than bewilderment in his voice. He looked at the shades as if he saw them for the first time. They were of vellum, or some substance near it, and upon each was painted a panorama of the right bank of the Seine, with the minute windows of the buildings cut out, under the direction of a superior mind, so that light might come through. 'What's the matter with them, Kit?'

'Dearest, if you don't know, I can't ever explain it to you,' she said. 'Among other things, they're banal, inappropriate, and unbeautiful. They're exactly what Evie Maynard *would* have chosen. She thinks, just because they show views of Paris, that they're pretty darned sophisticated. She is that not uncommon type of woman that thinks any reference to la belle France is an invitation to the waltz. "Not uncommon". If that isn't the mildest word-picture that ever was painted of that — '

'Don't you like the way she decorated the apartment?' he said.

'Sweetheart,' she said, 'I think it's poisonous. You know that.'

'Would you like to do it over?' he said.

'I should say not,' she said. 'Look, Hobie, don't you remember me? I'm the one that doesn't want to decorate your flat. Now do you place me? But if I ever *did*, the first thing I should do would be to paint these walls putty colour – no, I guess first I'd tear off all this chintz and fling it to the winds, and then I'd — '

The telephone rang . . .

The young man threw one stricken glance at the young woman and then sat motionless. The jangles of the bell cut the dusk like little scissors.

'I think', said the young woman, exquisitely, 'that your telephone is ringing. Don't let me keep you from answering it. As a matter of fact, I really must go powder my nose.'

She sprang up, dashed through the bedroom, and into the bathroom. There was the sound of a closed door, the grind of a firmly turned key, and then immediately the noise of rushing waters.

When she returned, eventually, to the living-room, the young man was pouring a pale, cold liquid into small glasses. He gave one to her, and smiled at her over it. It was his wistful smile. It was of his best.

'Hobie,' she said, 'is there a livery stable anywhere around here where they rent wild horses?'

'What?' he said.

'Because if there is,' she said, 'I wish you'd call up and ask them to send over a couple of teams. I want to show you they couldn't drag me into asking who that was on the telephone.'

'Oh,' he said, and tried his cocktail. 'Is this dry enough, sweet? Because you like them dry, don't you? Sure it's all right? Really? Ah, wait a second, darling. Let *me* light your cigarette. There. Sure you're all right?'

'I can't stand it,' she said. 'I just lost all my strength of purpose – maybe the maid will find it on the floor in the morning. Hobart Ogden, who was that on the telephone?'

'Oh, that?' he said. 'Well, that was a certain lady who shall be nameless.'

'I'm sure she should be,' she said. 'She doubtless has all the other qualities of a – Well. I didn't quite say it, I'm keeping my head. Ah, dearest, was that Connie Holt again?'

'No, that was the funniest thing,' he said. 'That was Evie Maynard. Just when we were talking about her.'

'Well, well, well,' she said. 'Isn't it a small world? And what's on her mind, if I may so flatter her? Is *her* butler tight, too?'

'Evie hasn't got a butler,' he said. He tried smiling again, but found it better to abandon the idea and concentrate on refilling the young woman's glass. 'No, she's just dizzy, the same as usual. She's got a cocktail party at her apartment, and they all want to go out on the town, that's all.'

'Luckily,' she said, 'you had to go out with these friends of your sister's. You were just going out the door when she called.'

'I never told her any such thing!' he said. 'I said I had a date I'd been looking forward to all week.'

'Oh, you didn't mention any names?' she said.

'There's no reason why I should, to Evie Maynard,' he said. 'It's none of her affair, any more than what she's doing and who she's doing it with is any concern of mine. She's nothing in my life. You know that. I've hardly seen her since she did the apartment. I don't care if I never see her again. I'd *rather* I never saw her again.'

'I should think that might be managed, if you've really set your heart on it,' she said.

'Well, I do what I can,' he said. 'She wanted to come in

now for a cocktail, she and some of those interior decorator boys she has with her, and I told her absolutely no.'

'And you think that will keep her away?' she said. 'Oh, no. She'll be here. She and her feathered friends. Let's see – they ought to arrive just about the time that Mrs Holt has thought it over and come into town. Well. It's shaping up into a lovely evening, isn't it?'

'Great,' he said. 'And if I may say so, you're doing everything you can to make it harder, you little sweet.' He poured more cocktails. 'O Kit, why are you being so nasty? Don't do it, darling. It's not like you. It's so unbecoming to you.'

'I know it's horrible,' she said. 'It's – well, I do it in defence, I suppose, Hobie. If I didn't say nasty things, I'd cry. I'm afraid to cry; it would take me so long to stop. I – oh, I'm so hurt, dear. I don't know what to think. All these women. All these awful women. If they were fine, if they were sweet and gentle and intelligent, I shouldn't mind. Or maybe I should. I don't know. I don't know much of anything, any more. My mind goes round and round. I thought what we had was so different. Well – it wasn't. Sometimes I think it would be better never to see you any more. But then I know I couldn't stand that. I'm too far gone now. I'd do anything to be with you! And so I'm just another of those women to you. And I used to come first, Hobie – oh, I did! I did!'

'You did!' he said. 'And you do!'

'And I always will?' she said.

'And you always will,' he said, 'as long as you'll only be your own self. Please be sweet again, Kit. Like this, darling. Like this, child.'

Again they were close, and again there was no sound.

The telephone rang.

They started as if the same arrow had pierced them. Then the young woman moved slowly back.

'You know,' she said, musingly, 'this is my fault. I did this. It was me. I was the one that said let's meet here, and not at my house. I said it would be quieter, and I had so much I wanted to talk to you about. I said we could be quiet and alone here. Yes. I said that.'

'I give you my word,' he said, 'that damn thing hasn't rung in a week.'

'It was lucky for me, wasn't it?' she said, 'that I happened to be here the last time it did. I am known as Little Miss Horse-shoes. Well. Oh, please do answer it, Hobie. It drives me even crazier to have it ring like this.'

'I hope to God', the young man said, 'that it's a wrong number.' He held her to him, hard. 'Darling,' he said. Then he went to the telephone.

'Hello,' he said into the receiver. 'Yes? Oh, hello there. How are you, dear – how are you? Oh, did you? Ah, that's too bad. Why, you see I was out with these friends of my – I was out till quite late. Oh, you did? Oh, that's too bad, dear, you waited up all that time. No, I did *not* say that, Margot, I said I'd come if I possibly could. That's exactly what I said. I did so. Well, then you misunderstood me. Well, you must have. Now, there's no need to be unreasonable about it. Listen, what I said, I said I'd come if it was possible, but I didn't think there was a chance. If you think hard, you'll remember, dear. Well, I'm terribly sorry, but I don't see what you're making so much fuss about. It was just a misunderstanding, that's all. Why don't you calm down and be a good little girl? Won't you? Why, I can't tonight, dear. Because I *can't*. Well, I have a date I've had for a long time. Yes. Oh, no, it isn't anything like that! Oh, now, please, Margot! Margot, please don't! Now don't do that! I tell you I won't be here. All right, come ahead, but I won't be in. Listen, I can't talk to you when you're like this. I'll call you tomorrow, dear. I tell you I won't be *in*, dear! Please be good. Certainly I do. Look. I have to run now. I'll call you, dear. 'Bye.'

The young man came back to the living-room, and sent his somewhat shaken voice ahead of him.

'How about another cocktail, sweet?' he said. 'Don't you think we really ought—' Through the thickening dark, he saw the young woman. She stood straight and tense. Her fur scarf was knotted about her shoulders, and she was drawing on her second glove.

'What's this about?' the young man said.

'I'm so sorry,' the young woman said, 'but I truly must go home.'

'Oh, really?' he said. 'May I ask why?'

'It's sweet of you', she said, 'to be interested enough to want to know. Thank you so much. Well, it just happens, I can't stand any more of this. There is somewhere, I think, some proverb about a worm's eventually turning. It is doubtless from the Arabic. They so often are. Well, good-night, Hobie, and thank you so much for those delicious cocktails. They've cheered me up wonderfully.'

She held out her hand. He caught it tight in both of his.

'Ah, now listen,' he said. 'Please don't do this, Kit. Please, don't, darling. Please. This is just the way you were last Wednesday.'

'Yes,' she said. 'And for exactly the same reason. Please give me back my hand. Thank you. Well, good-night, Hobie, and good luck, always.'

'All right,' he said. 'If this is what you want to do.'

'Want to do!' she said. 'It's nothing *I* want. I simply felt it would be rather easier for you if you could be alone, to receive your telephone calls. Surely you cannot blame me for feeling a bit *de trop*.'

'My Lord, do you think I want to talk to those fools?' he said. 'What can I do? Take the telephone receiver off? Is that what you want me to do?'

'It's a good trick of yours,' she said. 'I gather that was what you did last Wednesday night, when I kept trying to call you after I'd gone home, when I was in holy agony there.'

'I did not!' he said. 'They must have been calling the wrong number. I tell you I was alone here all the time you were gone.'

'So you said,' she said.

'I don't lie to you, Kit,' he said.

'That', she said, 'is the most outrageous lie you have ever told me. Good-night, Hobie.'

Only from the young man's eyes and voice could his anger be judged. The beautiful scroll of his mouth never straightened. He took her hand and bowed over it.

'Good-night, Kit,' he said.

'Good-night,' she said. 'Well, good-night. I'm sorry it must end like this. But if you want other things – well, they're what you want. You can't have both them and me. Good-night, Hobie.'

'Good-night, Kit,' he said.

'I'm sorry,' she said. 'It does seem too bad. Doesn't it?'

'It's what you want,' he said.

'I?' she said. 'It's what *you* do.'

'O Kit, can't you understand?' he said. 'You always used to. Don't you know how I am? I just say things and do things that don't mean anything, just for the sake of peace, just for the sake of not having a feud. That's what gets me in trouble. You don't have to do it, I know. You're luckier than I am.'

'Luckier?' she said. 'Curious word.'

'Well, stronger, then,' he said. 'Finer. Honester. Decenter. All those. Ah, don't do this, Kit. Please. Please take those things off, and come sit down.'

'Sit down?' she said. 'And wait for the ladies to gather?'

'They're not coming,' he said.

'How do you know?' she said. 'They've come here before, haven't they! How do you know they won't come tonight?'

'I don't know!' he said. 'I don't know what the hell they'll do. I don't know what the hell you'll do, any more. And I thought you were different!'

'I was different,' she said, 'just so long as you thought I was different.'

'Ah, Kit,' he said, 'Kit. Darling. Come and be the way we were. Come and be sweet and peaceful. Look. Let's have a cocktail, just to each other, and then let's go out to some quiet place for dinner, where we can talk. Will you?'

'Well – ' she said. 'If you think — '

'I think,' he said.

The telephone rang.

'Oh, my *God*!' shrieked the young woman. 'Go answer it, you damned – you damned *stallion*!'

She rushed for the door, opened it, and was gone. She was,

after all, different. She neither slammed the door nor left it stark open.

The young man stood, and he shook his remarkable head slowly. Slowly, too, he turned and went into the bedroom.

He spoke into the telephone receiver drearily at first, then he seemed to enjoy both hearing and speaking. He used a woman's name in address. It was not Connie; it was not Evie; it was not Margot. Glowingly he besought the unseen one to meet him; tepidly he agreed to await her coming where he was. He besought her, then, to ring his bell first three times and then twice, for admission. No, no, no, he said, this was not for any reason that might have occurred to her; it was simply that some business friend of his had said something about dropping in, and he wanted to make sure there would be no such intruders. He spoke of his hopes, indeed his assurances, of an evening of sweetness and peace. He said 'goodbye', and he said 'dear'.

The very good-looking young man hung up the receiver, and looked long at the dial of his wrist-watch, now delicately luminous. He seemed to be calculating. So long for a young woman to reach her home, and fling herself upon her couch, so long for tears, so long for exhaustion, so long for remorse, so long for rising tenderness. Thoughtfully he lifted the receiver from its hook and set it on end upon the little table.

Then he went into the living-room, and sped the dark before the tiny beams that sifted through the little open windows in the panoramas of Paris.

Comment

Oh, life is a glorious cycle of song,
A medley of extemporanea;
And love is a thing that can never go wrong;
And I am Marie of Romania.

Incurable

And if my heart be scarred and burned,
The safer, I, for all I learned;
The calmer, I, to see it true
That ways of love are never new –
The love that sets you daft and dazed
Is every love that ever blazed;
The happier, I, to fathom this:
A kiss is every other kiss.
The reckless vow, the lovely name,
When Helen walked, were spoke the same;
The weighted breast, the grinding woe,
When Phaon fled, were ever so.
Oh, it is sure as it is sad
That any lad is every lad,
And what's a girl, to dare implore
Her dear be hers forevermore?
Though he be tried and he be bold,
And swearing death should he be cold,
He'll run the path the others went . . .
But you, my sweet, are different.

The Second Oldest Story

Go I must along my ways
   Though my heart be ragged,
Dripping bitter through the days,
   Festering, and jagged.
Smile I must at every twinge,
   Kiss, to time its throbbing;
He that tears a heart to fringe
   Hates the noise of sobbing.

. . . .

Weep, my love, till Heaven hears;
   Curse and moan and languish.
While I wash your wound with tears,
   Ease aloud your anguish.
Bellow of the pit in Hell
   Where you're made to linger.
There and there and well and well –
   Did he prick his finger!

Ballade at Thirty-Five

This, no song of an ingénue,
  This, no ballad of innocence;
This, the rhyme of a lady who
  Followed ever her natural bents.
  This, a solo of sapience,
This, a chantey of sophistry,
  This, the sum of experiments –
I loved them until they loved me.

Decked in garments of sable hue,
  Daubed with ashes of myriad Lents,
Wearing shower bouquets of rue,
  Walk I ever in penitence.
  Oft I roam, as my heart repents,
Through God's acre of memory,
  Marking stones, in my reverence,
'I loved them until they loved me.'

Pictures pass me in long review –
  Marching columns of dead events.
I was tender and, often, true;
  Ever a prey to coincidence.
  Always knew I the consequence;
Always saw what the end would be.
  We're as Nature has made us – hence
I loved them until they loved me.

L'envoi
Princes, never I'd give offence
  Won't you think of me tenderly?
Here's my strength and my weakness, gents –
  I loved them until they loved me.

YOU WERE PERFECTLY FINE

The pale young man eased himself carefully into the low chair, and rolled his head to the side, so that the cool chintz comforted his cheek and temple.

'Oh, dear,' he said. 'Oh, dear, oh, dear, oh, dear. Oh.'

The clear-eyed girl, sitting light and erect on the couch, smiled brightly at him.

'Not feeling so well today?' she said.

'Oh, I'm great,' he said. 'Corking, I am. Know what time I got up? Four o'clock this afternoon, sharp. I kept trying to make it, and every time I took my head off the pillow, it would roll under the bed. This isn't my head I've got on now. I think this is something that used to belong to Walt Whitman. Oh, dear, oh, dear, oh, dear.'

'Do you think maybe a drink would make you feel better?' she said.

'The hair of the mastiff that bit me?' he said. 'Oh, no, thank you. Please never speak of anything like that again. I'm through. I'm all, all through. Look at that hand; steady as a humming-bird. Tell me, was I very terrible last night?'

'Oh, goodness,' she said, 'everybody was feeling pretty high. You were all right.'

'Yeah,' he said. 'I must have been dandy. Is everybody sore at me?'

'Good Heavens, no,' she said. 'Everyone thought you were terribly funny. Of course, Jim Pierson was a little stuffy, there, for a minute at dinner. But people sort of held him back in his chair, and got him calmed down. I don't think anybody at the other tables noticed it at all. Hardly anybody.'

'He was going to sock me?' he said. 'O Lord. What did I do to him?'

'Why, you didn't do a thing,' she said. 'You were perfectly fine. But you know how silly Jim gets, when he thinks anybody is making too much fuss over Elinor.'

'Was I making a pass at Elinor?' he said. 'Did I do that?'

'Of course you didn't,' she said. 'You were only fooling,

that's all. She thought you were awfully amusing. She was having a marvellous time. She only got a little tiny bit annoyed just once, when you poured the clam-juice down her back.'

'My God,' he said. 'Clam-juice down that back. And every vertebra a little Cabot. Dear God. What'll I ever do?'

'Oh, she'll be all right,' she said. 'Just send her some flowers, or something. Don't worry about it. It isn't anything.'

'No, I won't worry,' he said. 'I haven't got a care in the world. I'm sitting pretty. Oh, dear, oh, dear. Did I do any other fascinating tricks at dinner?'

'You were fine,' she said. 'Don't be so foolish about it. Everybody was crazy about you. The *maître d'hôtel* was a little worried because you wouldn't stop singing, but he really didn't mind. All he said was, he was afraid they'd close the place again, if there was so much noise. But he didn't care a bit, himself. I think he loved seeing you have such a good time. Oh, you were just singing away, there, for about an hour. It wasn't so terribly loud, at all.'

'So I sang,' he said. 'That must have been a treat. I sang.'

'Don't you remember?' she said. 'You just sang one song after another. Everybody in the place was listening. They loved it. Only you kept insisting that you wanted to sing some song about some kind of fusiliers or other, and everybody kept shushing you, and you'd keep trying to start it again. You were wonderful. We were all trying to make you stop singing for a minute, and eat something, but you wouldn't hear of it. My, you were funny.'

'Didn't I eat any dinner?' he said.

'Oh, not a thing,' she said. 'Every time the waiter would offer you something, you'd give it right back to him, because you said that he was your long-lost brother, changed in the cradle by a gypsy band, and that anything you had was his. You had him simply roaring at you.'

'I bet I did,' he said. 'I bet I was comical. Society's Pet, I must have been. And what happened then, after my overwhelming success with the waiter?'

'Why, nothing much,' she said. 'You took a sort of dislike

to some old man with white hair, sitting across the room, because you didn't like his necktie and you wanted to tell him about it. But we got you out, before he got really mad.'

'Oh, we got out,' he said. 'Did I walk?'

'Walk! Of course you did,' she said. 'You were absolutely all right. There was that nasty stretch of ice on the sidewalk, and you did sit down awfully hard, you poor dear. But good Heavens, that might have happened to anybody.'

'Oh, sure,' he said. 'Louisa Alcott or anybody. So I fell down on the sidewalk. That would explain what's the matter with my – Yes. I see. And then what, if you don't mind?'

'Ah, now, Peter!' she said. 'You can't sit there and say you don't remember what happened after that! I did think that maybe you were just a little tight at dinner – oh, you were perfectly all right, and all that, but I did know you were feeling pretty gay. But you were so serious, from the time you fell down – I never knew you to be that way. Don't you know, how you told me I had never seen your real self before? Oh, Peter, I just couldn't bear it, if you didn't remember that lovely long ride we took together in the taxi! Please, you do remember that, don't you? I think it would simply kill me, if you didn't.'

'Oh, yes,' he said. 'Riding in the taxi. Oh, yes, sure. Pretty long ride, hmm?'

'Round and round and round the park,' she said. 'Oh, and the trees were shining so in the moonlight. And you said you never knew before that you really had a soul.'

'Yes,' he said. 'I said that. That was me.'

'You said such lovely, lovely things,' she said. 'And I'd never known, all this time, how you had been feeling about me, and I'd never dared to let you see how I felt about you. And then last night – oh, Peter dear, I think that taxi ride was the most important thing that ever happened to us in our lives.'

'Yes,' he said. 'I guess it must have been.'

'And we're going to be so happy,' she said. 'Oh, I just want to tell everybody! But I don't know – I think maybe it would be sweeter to keep it all to ourselves.'

'I think it would be,' he said.

'Isn't it lovely?' she said.

'Yes,' he said. 'Great.'

'Lovely!' she said.

'Look here,' he said, 'do you mind if I have a drink? I mean, just medicinally, you know. I'm off the stuff for life, so help me. But I think I feel a collapse coming on.'

'Oh, I think it would do you good,' she said. 'You poor boy, it's a shame you feel so awful. I'll go make you a whisky and soda.'

'Honestly,' he said, 'I don't see how you could ever want to speak to me again, after I made such a fool of myself, last night. I think I'd better go join a monastery in Tibet.'

'You crazy idiot!' she said. 'As if I could ever let you go away now! Stop talking like that. You were perfectly fine.'

She jumped up from the couch, kissed him quickly on the forehead, and ran out of the room.

The pale young man looked after her and shook his head long and slowly, then dropped it in his damp and trembling hands.

'Oh, dear,' he said. 'Oh, dear, oh, dear, oh, dear.'

A Pig's-eye View of Literature

The Lives and Times of John Keats, Percy Bysshe Shelley, and George Gordon Noel, Lord Byron

Byron and Shelley and Keats
Were a trio of lyrical treats.
The forehead of Shelley was cluttered with curls,
And Keats never was a descendant of earls,
And Byron walked out with a number of girls,
  But it didn't impair the poetical feats
    Of Byron and Shelley,
    Of Byron and Shelley,
  Of Byron and Shelley and Keats.

Oscar Wilde

If, with the literate, I am
Impelled to try an epigram,
I never seek to take the credit;
We all assume that Oscar said it.

Harriet Beecher Stowe

The pure and worthy Mrs Stowe
Is one we all are proud to know
As mother, wife, and authoress –
Thank God, I am content with less!

D. G. Rossetti

Dante Gabriel Rossetti
Buried all of his *libretti*,
Thought the matter over – then
Went and dug them up again.

Thomas Carlyle

Carlyle combined the lit'ry life
With throwing teacups at his wife,

Remarking, rather testily,
'Oh, stop your dodging, Mrs C!'

Charles Dickens

Who call him spurious and shoddy
Shall do it o'er my lifeless body.
I heartily invite such birds
To come outside and say those words!

Alexandre Dumas and his Son

Although I work, and seldom cease,
At Dumas *père* and Dumas *fils*,
Alas, I cannot make me care
For Dumas *fils* and Dumas *père*.

Alfred, Lord Tennyson

Should Heaven send me any son,
I hope he's not like Tennyson.
I'd rather have him play a fiddle
Than rise and bow and speak an idyll.

George Gissing

When I admit neglect of Gissing,
They say I don't know what I'm missing.
Until their arguments are subtler,
I think I'll stick to Samuel Butler.

Walter Savage Landor

Upon the work of Walter Landor
I am unfit to write with candour.
If you can read it, well and good;
But as for me, I never could.

George Sand

What time the gifted lady took
Away from paper, pen, and book,
She spent in amorous dalliance
(They do those things so well in France).

Victoria

Dear dead Victoria
  Rotted cosily;
In excelsis gloria,
  And R.I.P.

And her shroud was buttoned neat,
  And her bones were clean and round,
And her soul was at her feet
  Like a bishop's marble hound.

Albert lay a-drying,
  Lavishly arrayed,
With his soul out flying
  Where his heart had stayed.

And there's some could tell you what land
  His spirit walks serene
(But I've heard them say in Scotland
  It's never been seen).

Mortal Enemy

Let another cross his way –
  She's the one will do the weeping!
Little need I fear he'll stray
  Since I have his heart in keeping.

Let another hail him dear –
  Little chance that he'll forget me!
Only need I curse and fear
  Her he loved before he met me.

TOO BAD

'My dear,' Mrs Marshall said to Mrs Ames, 'I never was so surprised in my life. Never in my life. Why, Grace and I were like that – just like *that*.'

She held up her right hand, the upstanding first and second fingers rigidly close together, in illustration.

Mrs Ames shook her head sadly, and offered the cinnamon toast.

'Imagine!' said Mrs Marshall, refusing it though with a longing eye. 'We were going to have dinner with them last Tuesday night, and then I got this letter from Grace from this little place up in Connecticut, saying she was going to be up there she didn't know how long, and she thought, when she came back, she'd probably take just one big room with a kitchenette. Ernest was living down at the club, she said.'

'But what did they do about their apartment?' Mrs Ames's voice was high with anxiety.

'Why, it seems his sister took it, furnished and all – by the way, remind me, I must go and see her,' said Mrs Marshall. 'They wanted to move into town, anyway, and they were looking for a place.'

'Doesn't she feel terribly about it – his sister?' asked Mrs Ames.

'Oh – terribly.' Mrs Marshall dismissed the word as inadequate. 'My dear, think how everybody that knew them feels. Think how I feel. I don't know when I've had a thing depress me more. If it had been anybody but the Weldons!'

Mrs Ames nodded.

'That's what I said,' she reported.

'That's what everybody says.' Mrs Marshall quickly took away any undeserved credit. 'To think of the Weldons separating! Why, I always used to say to Jim, "Well, there's one happily married couple, anyway," I used to say, "so congenial, and with that nice apartment, and all." And then, right out of a clear sky, they go and separate. I simply can't understand what on earth made them do it. It just seems too awful!'

Again Mrs Ames nodded, slowly and sadly.

'Yes, it always seems too bad, a thing like that does,' she said. 'It's too bad.'

II

Mrs Ernest Weldon wandered about the orderly living-room, giving it some of those little feminine touches. She was not especially good as a touch-giver. The idea was pretty, and appealing to her. Before she was married, she had dreamed of herself as moving softly about her new dwelling, deftly moving a vase here or straightening a flower there, and thus transforming it from a house to a home. Even now, after seven years of marriage, she liked to picture herself in the gracious act.

But, though she conscientiously made a try at it every night as soon as the rose-shaded lamps were lit, she was always a bit bewildered as to how one went about performing those tiny miracles that make all the difference in the world to a room. The living-room, it seemed to her, looked good enough as it was – as good as it would ever look, with that mantelpiece and the same old furniture. Delia, one of the most thoroughly feminine of creatures, had subjected it to a long series of emphatic touches earlier in the day, and none of her handiwork had since been disturbed. But the feat of making all the difference in the world, so Mrs Weldon had always heard, was not a thing to be left to servants. Touch-giving was a wife's job. And Mrs Weldon was not one to shirk the business she had entered.

With an almost pitiable air of uncertainty, she strayed over to the mantel, lifted a small Japanese vase, and stood with it in her hand, gazing helplessly around the room. The white-enamelled bookcase caught her eye, and gratefully she crossed to it and set the vase upon it, carefully rearranging various ornaments to make room. To relieve the congestion, she took up a framed photograph of Mr Weldon's sister in evening gown and eyeglasses, again looked all about, and then set it timidly on the piano. She smoothed the piano-cover ingratiatingly, straightened the copies of 'A Day in Venice', 'To a Wild Rose', and Kreisler's 'Caprice Viennois', which stood ever upon the rack, walked over to the tea-table and effected a change of places between the cream-jug and the sugar-bowl.

Then she stepped back, and surveyed her innovations. It was amazing how little difference they made to the room.

Sighing, Mrs Weldon turned her attention to a bowl of daffodils, slightly past their first freshness. There was nothing to be done there; the omniscient Delia had refreshed them with clear water, had clipped their stems, and removed their more *passée* sisters. Still Mrs Weldon bent over them pulling them gently about.

She liked to think of herself as one for whom flowers would thrive, who must always have blossoms about her, if she would be truly happy. When her living-room flowers died, she almost never forgot to stop in at the florist's, the next day, and get a fresh bunch. She told people, in little bursts of confidence, that she loved flowers. There was something almost apologetic in her way of uttering her tender avowal, as if she would beg her listeners not to consider her too bizarre in her taste. It seemed rather as though she expected the hearer to fall back, startled, at her words, crying, 'Not really! Well, what *are* we coming to?'

She had other little confessions of affection, too, that she made from time to time; always with a little hesitation, as if understandably delicate about baring her heart, she told her love for colour, the country, a good time, a really interesting play, nice materials, well-made clothes, and sunshine. But it was her fondness for flowers that she acknowledged oftenest. She seemed to feel that this, even more than her other predilections, set her apart from the general.

Mrs Weldon gave the elderly daffodils a final pat, now, and once more surveyed the room, to see if any other repairs suggested themselves. Her lips tightened as the little Japanese vase met her gaze; distinctly, it had been better off in the first place. She set it back, the irritation that the sight of the mantel always gave her welling within her.

She had hated the mantelpiece from the moment they had first come to look at the apartment. There were other things that she had always hated about the place, too – the long, narrow hall, the dark dining-room, the inadequate closets. But Ernest had seemed to like the apartment well enough, so she had said nothing, then or since. After all, what was the use of fussing? Probably there would always be drawbacks, wherever they lived. There were enough in the last place they had had.

So they had taken the apartment on a five-year lease – there were four years and three months to go. Mrs Weldon felt suddenly weary. She lay down on the davenport, and pressed her thin hand against her dull brown hair.

Mr Weldon came down the street, bent almost double in his battle with the wind from the river. His mind went over its nightly dark thoughts on living near Riverside Drive, five blocks from a subway station – two of those blocks loud with savage gales. He did not much like their apartment, even when he reached it. As soon as he had seen that dining-room, he had realised that they must always breakfast by artificial light – a thing he hated. But Grace had never appeared to notice it, so he had held his peace. It didn't matter much, anyway, he explained to himself. There was pretty sure to be something wrong, everywhere. The dining-room wasn't much worse than that bedroom on the court, in the last place. Grace had never seemed to mind that, either.

Mrs Weldon opened the door at his ring.

'Well!' she said, cheerily.

They smiled brightly at each other.

'Hel-lo,' he said. 'Well! You home?'

They kissed, slightly. She watched with polite interest while he hung up his hat and coat, removed the evening papers from his pocket, and handed one to her.

'Bring the papers?' she said, taking it.

She preceded him along the narrow hall to the living-room, where he let himself slowly down into his big chair, with a sound between a sigh and a groan. She sat opposite him, on the davenport. Again they smiled brightly at each other.

'Well, what have you been doing with yourself today?' he enquired.

She had been expecting the question. She had planned

before he came in, how she would tell him all the little events of her day – how the woman in the grocer's shop had had an argument with the cashier, and how Delia had tried out a new salad for lunch with but moderate success, and how Alice Marshall had come to tea and it was quite true that Norma Matthews was going to have another baby. She had woven them into a lively little narrative, carefully choosing amusing phrases of description; had felt that she was going to tell it well and with spirit, and that he might laugh at the account of the occurrence in the grocer's. But now, as she considered it, it seemed to her a long, dull story. She had not the energy to begin it. And he was already smoothing out his paper.

'Oh, nothing,' she said, with a gay little laugh. 'Did you have a nice day?'

'Why—' he began. He had had some idea of telling her how he had finally put through that Detroit thing, and how tickled J.G. had seemed to be about it. But his interest waned, even as he started to speak. Besides, she was engrossed in breaking off a loose thread from the wool fringe on one of the pillows beside her.

'Oh, pretty fair,' he said.

'Tired?' she asked.

'Not so much,' he answered. 'Why – want to do anything tonight?'

'Why, not unless you do,' she said, brightly. 'Whatever you say.'

'Whatever *you* say,' he corrected her.

The subject closed. There was a third exchange of smiles, and then he hid most of himself behind his paper.

Mrs Weldon, too, turned to the newspaper. But it was an off night for news – a long speech of somebody's, a plan for a garbage dump, a proposed dirigible, a four-day-old murder mystery. No one she knew had died or become engaged or married, or had attended any social functions. The fashions depicted on the woman's page were for Miss Fourteen-to-Sixteen. The advertisements ran mostly to bread, and sauces, and men's clothes and sales of kitchen utensils. She put the paper down.

She wondered how Ernest could get so much enjoyment out of a newspaper. He could occupy himself with one for almost an hour, and then pick up another and go all through the same news with unabated interest. She wished that she could. She wished, even more than that, that she could think of something to say. She glanced around the room for inspiration.

'See my pretty daffy-down-dillies?' she said, finding it. To anyone else, she would have referred to them as daffodils.

Mr Weldon looked in the direction of the flowers.

'M-m-mm,' he said in admission, and returned to the news.

She looked at him, and shook her head despondently. He did not see, behind the paper; nor did she see that he was not reading. He was waiting, his hands gripping the printed sheet till their knuckles were blue-white, for her next remark.

It came.

'I love flowers,' she said, in one of her little rushes of confidence.

Her husband did not answer. He sighed, his grip relaxed, and he went on reading.

Mrs Weldon searched the room for another suggestion.

'Ernie,' she said, 'I'm so comfortable. Wouldn't you like to get up and get my handkerchief off the piano for me?'

He rose instantly. 'Why, certainly,' he said.

The way to ask people to fetch handkerchiefs, he thought as he went back to his chair, was to ask them to do it, and not try to make them think that you were giving them a treat. Either come right out and ask them, would they or wouldn't they, or else get up and get your handkerchief yourself.

'Thank you ever so much,' his wife said with enthusiasm.

Delia appeared in the doorway. 'Dinner,' she murmured bashfully, as if it were not quite a nice word for a young woman to use, and vanished.

'Dinner, Ern,' cried Mrs Weldon gaily, getting up.

'Just a minute,' issued indistinctly from behind the newspaper.

Mrs Weldon waited. Then her lips compressed, and she

went over and playfully took the paper from her husband's hands. She smiled carefully at him, and he smiled back at her.

'You go ahead in,' he said, rising. 'I'll be right with you. I've just got to wash up.'

She looked after him, and something like a volcanic eruption took place within her. You'd think that just one night – just one little night – he might go and wash before dinner was announced. Just one night – it didn't seem much to ask. But she said nothing. God knew it was aggravating, but after all, it wasn't worth the trouble of fussing about.

She was waiting, cheerful and bright, courteously refraining from beginning her soup, when he took his place at the table.

'Oh, tomato soup, eh?' he said.

'Yes,' she answered. 'You like it, don't you?'

'Who – me?' he said. 'Oh, yes. Yes, indeed.'

She smiled at him.

'Yes, I thought you liked it,' she said.

'You like it, too, don't you?' he enquired.

'Oh, yes,' she assured him. 'Yes, I like it ever so much. I'm awfully fond of tomato soup.'

'Yes,' he said, 'there's nothing much better than tomato soup on a cold night.'

She nodded.

'I think it's nice, too,' she confided.

They had had tomato soup for dinner probably three times a month during their married life.

The soup was finished, and Delia brought in the meat.

'Well, that looks pretty good,' said Mr Weldon, carving it. 'We haven't had steak for a long time.'

'Why, yes, we have, too, Ern,' his wife said eagerly. 'We had it – let me see, what night were the Baileys here? – we had it Wednesday night – no, Thursday night. Don't you remember?'

'Did we?' he said. 'Yes, I guess you're right. It seemed longer, somehow.'

Mrs Weldon smiled politely. She could not think of any way to prolong the discussion.

What did married people talk about, anyway, when they were alone together? She had seen married couples – not dubious ones but people she really knew were husbands and wives – at the theatre or in trains, talking together as animatedly as if they were just acquaintances. She always watched them, marvellingly, wondering what on earth they found to say.

She could talk well enough to other people. There never seemed to be enough time for her to finish saying all she wanted to to her friends; she recalled how she had run on to Alice Marshall, only that afternoon. Both men and women found her attractive to listen to; not brilliant, not particularly funny, but still amusing and agreeable. She was never at a loss for something to say, never conscious of groping around for a topic. She had a good memory for bits of fresh gossip, or little stories of some celebrity that she had read or heard somewhere, and a knack of telling them entertainingly. Things people said to her stimulated her to quick replies, and more amusing narratives. They weren't especially scintillating people, either; it was just that they talked to her.

That was the trick of it. If nobody said anything to you, how were you to carry on a conversation from there? Inside, she was always bitter and angry at Ernest for not helping her out.

Ernest, too, seemed to be talkative enough when he was with others. People were always coming up and telling her how much they had enjoyed meeting her husband, and what fun he was. They weren't just being polite. There was no reason why they should go out of their way to say it.

Even when she and Ernest had another couple in to dinner or bridge, they both talked and laughed easily, all evening long. But as soon as the guests said good-night and what an awfully nice evening it had been, and the door had closed behind them, there the Weldons were again, without a word to say to each other. It would have been intimate and amusing to have talked over their guests' clothes and skill at bridge and probable domestic and financial affairs, and she would do it the next day, with great interest, too, to Alice Marshall, or some other one of her friends. But she couldn't do it with Ernest. Just

WELL
YES!
REALLY?
NO

as she started to, she found she simply couldn't make the effort.

So they would put away the card-table and empty the ash-receivers, with many 'Oh, I beg your pardons' and 'No, no – I was in your ways', and then Ernest would say, 'Well, I guess I'll go along to bed,' and she would answer, 'All right – I'll be in in a minute,' and they would smile cheerfully at each other, and another evening would be over.

She tried to remember what they used to talk about before they were married, when they were engaged. It seemed to her that they never had had much to say to each other. But she hadn't worried about it then; indeed, she had felt the satisfaction of the correct, in their courtship, for she had always heard that true love was inarticulate. Then, besides, there had been always kissing and things, to take up your mind. But it had turned out that true marriage was apparently equally dumb. And you can't depend on kisses and all the rest of it to while away the evenings, after seven years.

You'd think that you would get used to it, in seven years, would realise that that was the way it was, and let it go at that. You don't, though. A thing like that gets on your nerves. It isn't one of those cosy, companionable silences that people occasionally fall into together. It makes you feel as if you must do something about it, as if you weren't performing your duty. You have the feeling a hostess has when her party is going badly, when her guests sit in corners and refuse to mingle. It makes you nervous and self-conscious, and you talk desperately about tomato soup, and say things like 'daffy-down-dilly'.

Mrs Weldon cast about in her mind for a subject to offer her husband. There was Alice Marshall's new system of reducing – no, that was pretty dull. There was the case she had read in the morning's paper about the man of eighty-seven who had taken, as his fourth wife, a girl of twenty – he had probably seen that, and as long as he hadn't thought it worth repeating, he wouldn't think it worth hearing. There was the thing the Baileys' little boy had said about Jesus – no, she had told him that the night before.

She looked over at him, desultorily eating his rhubarb pie.

She wished he wouldn't put that greasy stuff on his head. Perhaps it was necessary, if his hair really was falling out, but it did seem that he might find some more attractive remedy, if he only had the consideration to look around for one. Anyway, why must his hair fall out? There was something a little disgusting about people with falling hair.

'Like your pie, Ernie?' she asked vivaciously.

'Why, I don't know,' he said, thinking it over. 'I'm not so crazy about rhubarb, I don't think. Are you?'

'No, I'm not so awfully crazy about it,' she answered. 'But then, I'm not really crazy about any kind of pie.'

'Aren't you really?' he said, politely surprised. 'I like pie pretty well – some kinds of pie.'

'Do you?' The polite surprise was hers now.

'Why, yes,' he said. 'I like a nice huckleberry pie, or a nice lemon meringue pie, or a—' He lost interest in the thing himself, and his voice died away.

He avoided looking at her left hand, which lay on the edge of the table, palm upward. The long, grey-white ends of her nails protruded beyond the tips of her fingers, and the sight made him uncomfortable. Why in God's name must she wear her finger-nails that preposterous length, and file them to those horrible points? If there was anything that he hated, it was a woman with pointed finger-nails.

They returned to the living-room, and Mr Weldon again eased himself down into the chair, reaching for the second paper.

'Quite sure there isn't anything you'd like to do tonight?' he asked solicitously. 'Like to go to the movies, or anything?'

'Oh, no,' she said. 'Unless there's something you want to do.'

'No, no,' he answered. 'I just thought maybe you wanted to.'

'Not unless you do,' she said.

He began on his paper, and she wandered aimlessly about the room. She had forgotten to get a new book from the library, and it had never in her life occurred to her to reread a book that she had once completed. She thought vaguely of playing solitaire, but she did not care enough about it to go to the trouble of getting out the cards, and setting up the table. There was some sewing that she could do, and she thought that she might presently go into the bedroom and fetch the night-gown that she was making for herself. Yes, she would probably do that, in a little while.

Ernest would read industriously, and, along toward the middle of the paper, he would start yawning aloud. Something happened inside Mrs Weldon when he did this. She would murmur that she had to speak to Delia, and hurry to the kitchen. She would stay there rather a long time, looking vaguely into jars and enquiring half-heartedly about laundry lists, and, when she returned, he would have gone in to get ready for bed.

In a year, three hundred of their evenings were like this. Seven times three hundred is more than two thousand.

Mrs Weldon went into the bedroom, and brought back her sewing. She sat down, pinned the pink satin to her knee, and began whipping narrow lace along the top of the half-made garment. It was fussy work. The fine thread knotted and drew, and she could not get the light adjusted so that the shadow of her head did not fall on her work. She grew a little sick, from the strain on her eyes.

Mr Weldon turned a page, and yawned aloud. 'Wah-huh-huh-huh-huh,' he went, on a descending scale. He yawned again, and this time climbed the scale.

III

'My dear,' Mrs Ames said to Mrs Marshall, 'don't you really think that there must have been some other woman?'

'Oh, I simply couldn't think it was anything like that,' said Mrs Marshall. 'Not Ernest Weldon. So devoted – home every night at half-past six, and such good company, and so jolly, and all. I don't see how there *could* have been.'

'Sometimes', observed Mrs Ames, 'those awfully jolly men at home are just the kind.'

'Yes, I know,' Mrs Marshall said. 'But not Ernest Weldon.

Why, I used to say to Jim, "I never saw such a devoted husband in my life," I said. Oh, not Ernest Weldon.'

'I don't suppose,' began Mrs Ames, and hesitated. 'I don't suppose', she went on, intently pressing the bit of sodden lemon in her cup with her teaspoon, 'that Grace – that there was ever anyone – or anything like that?'

'Oh, Heavens, no,' cried Mrs Marshall. 'Grace Weldon just gave her whole life to that man. It was Ernest this and Ernest that every minute. I simply can't understand it. If there was one earthly reason – if they ever fought, or if Ernest drank, or anything like that. But they got along so beautifully together – why, it just seems as if they must have been crazy to go and do a thing like this. Well, I can't begin to tell you how blue it's made me. It seems so awful!'

'Yes,' said Mrs Ames, 'it certainly is too bad.'

Story

'And if he's gone away,' said she,
'Good riddance, if you're asking me.
I'm not a one to lie awake
And weep for anybody's sake.
There's better lads than him about!
I'll wear my buckled slippers out
A-dancing till the break of day.
I'm better off with him away!
And if he never come,' said she,
'Now what on earth is that to me?
I wouldn't have him back!'
I hope
Her mother washed her mouth with soap.

Fable

Oh, there once was a lady, and so I've been told,
Whose lover grew weary, whose lover grew cold.
'My child,' he remarked, 'though our episode ends,
In the manner of men, I suggest we be friends.'
And the truest of friends ever after they were –
Oh, they lied in their teeth when they told me of her!

Bohemia

Authors and actors and artists and such
Never know nothing, and never know much.
Sculptors and singers and those of their kidney
Tell their affairs from Seattle to Sydney.
Playwrights and poets and such horses' necks
Start off from anywhere, end up at sex.
Diarists, critics, and similar roe
Never say nothing, and never say no.
People Who Do Things exceed my endurance;
God, for a man that solicits insurance!

Surprise

My heart went fluttering with fear
Lest you should go, and leave me here
To beat my breast and rock my head
And stretch me sleepless on my bed.
Ah, clear they see and true they say
That one shall weep, and one shall stray
For such is Love's unvarying law . . .
I never thought, I never saw
That I should be the first to go;
How pleasant that it happened so!

Dilemma

If I were mild, and I were sweet,
And laid my heart before your feet,
And took my dearest thoughts to you,
And hailed your easy lies as true;
Were I to murmur 'Yes', and then
'How true, my dear', and 'Yes', again,
And wear my eyes discreetly down,
And tremble whitely at your frown,
And keep my words unquestioning –
My love, you'd run like anything!

Should I be frail, and I be mad,
And share my heart with every lad,
But beat my head against the floor
What times you wandered past my door;
Were I to doubt, and I to sneer,
And shriek 'Farewell!' and still be here,
And break your joy, and quench your trust –
I should not see you for the dust!

Unfortunate Coincidence

By the time you swear you're his,
   Shivering and sighing,
And he vows his passion is
   Infinite, undying –
Lady, make a note of this:
   One of you is lying.

JUST A LITTLE ONE

I like this place, Fred. This is a nice place. How did you ever find it? I think you're perfectly marvellous, discovering a speakeasy in the year 1928. And they let you right in, without asking you a single question. I bet you could get into the subway without using anybody's name. Couldn't you, Fred?

Oh, I like this place better and better, now that my eyes are getting accustomed to it. You mustn't let them tell you this lighting system is original with them, Fred; they got the idea from the Mammoth Cave. This is you sitting next to me, isn't it? Oh, you can't fool me. I'd know that knee anywhere.

You know what I like about this place? It's got atmosphere. That's what it's got. If you would ask the waiter to bring a fairly sharp knife, I could cut off a nice little block of the atmosphere, to take home with me. It would be interesting to have for my memory book. I'm going to start keeping a memory book tomorrow. Don't let me forget.

Why, I don't know, Fred – what are you going to have? Then I guess I'll have a highball, too; please, just a little one. Is it really real Scotch? Well, that will be a new experience for me. You ought to see the Scotch I've got home in my cupboard; at least it was in the cupboard this morning – it's probably eaten its way out by now. I got it for my birthday. Well, it was something. The birthday before, all I got was a year older.

This is a nice highball, isn't it? Well, well, well, to think of me having real Scotch; I'm out of the bush leagues at last. Are you going to have another one? Well, I shouldn't like to see you drinking all by yourself, Fred. Solitary drinking is what causes half the crime in the country. That's what's responsible for the failure of prohibition. But please, Fred, tell him to make mine just a little one. Make it awfully weak; just cambric Scotch.

It will be nice to see the effect of veritable whisky upon one who has been accustomed only to the simpler forms of entertainment. You'll like that, Fred. You'll stay by me if anything happens, won't you? I don't think there will be anything spectacular, but I want to ask you one thing, just in case. Don't let me take any horses home with me. It doesn't matter so much about stray dogs and kittens, but elevator boys get awfully stuffy when you try to bring in a horse. You might just as well know that about me now, Fred. You can always tell that the crash is coming when I start getting tender about Our Dumb Friends. Three highballs, and I think I'm St Francis of Assisi.

But I don't believe anything is going to happen to me on these. That's because they're made of real stuff. That's what the difference is. This just makes you feel fine. Oh, I feel swell, Fred. You do too, don't you? I knew you did, because you look better. I love that tie you have on. Oh, did Edith give it to you? Ah, wasn't that nice of her? You know, Fred, most people are really awfully nice. There are darn few that aren't pretty fine at heart. You've got a beautiful heart, Fred. You'd be the first person I'd go to if I were in trouble. I guess you are just about the best friend I've got in the world. But I worry about you, Fred. I do so, too. I don't think you take enough care of yourself. You ought to take care of yourself for your friends' sake. You oughtn't to drink all this terrible stuff that's around; you owe it to your friends to be careful. You don't mind my talking to you like this, do you? You see, dear, it's because I'm your friend that I hate to see you not taking care of yourself. It hurts me to see you batting around the way you've been doing. You ought to stick to this place, where they have real Scotch that can't do you any harm. Oh, darling, do you really think I ought to? Well, you tell him just a little bit of a one. Tell him, sweet.

Do you come here often, Fred? I shouldn't worry about you so much if I knew you were in a safe place like this. Oh, is this where you were Thursday night? I see. Why, no, it didn't make a bit of difference, only you told me to call you up, and like a fool I broke a date I had, just because I thought I was going to see you. I just sort of naturally thought so, when you said to call you up. Oh, good Lord, don't make all that fuss about it. It really didn't make the slightest difference. It just didn't seem a very friendly way to behave, that's all. I don't know – I'd been believing we were such good friends. I'm an awful idiot about people, Fred. There aren't many who are really your friend at heart.

Practically anybody would play you dirt for a nickel. Oh, yes, they would.

Was Edith here with you, Thursday night? This place must be very becoming to her. Next to being in a coal mine, I can't think of anywhere she could go that the light would be more flattering to that pan of hers. Do you really know a lot of people that say she's good-looking? You must have a wide acquaintance among the astigmatic, haven't you, Freddie, dear? Why, I'm not being any way at all – it's simply one of those things, either you can see it or you can't. Now to me, Edith looks like something that would eat her young. Dresses well? *Edith* dresses well? Are you trying to kid me, Fred, at my age? You mean you mean it? Oh, my God. You mean those clothes of hers are *intentional*? My Heavens, I always thought she was on her way out of a burning building.

Well, we live and learn. Edith dresses well! Edith's got good taste! Yes, she's got sweet taste in neckties. I don't suppose I ought to say it about such a dear friend of yours, Fred, but she is the lousiest necktie-picker-out I ever saw. I never saw anything could touch that thing you have around your neck. All right, suppose I did say I liked it. I just said that because I felt sorry for you. I'd feel sorry for anybody with a thing like that on. I just wanted to try to make you feel good, because I thought you were my friend. My friend! I haven't got a friend in the world. Do you know that, Fred? Not one single friend in this world.

All right, what do you care if I'm crying? I can cry if I want to, can't I? I guess you'd cry, too, if you didn't have a friend in the world. Is my face very bad? I suppose that damned mascara has run all over it. I've got to give up using mascara, Fred; life's too sad. Isn't life terrible? Oh, my God, isn't life awful? Ah, don't cry, Fred. Please don't. Don't you care, baby. Life's terrible, but don't you care. You've got friends. I'm the one that hasn't got any friends. I am so. No, it's me. I'm the one.

I don't think another drink would make me feel any better. I don't know whether I want to feel any better. What's the sense of feeling good, when life's so terrible? Oh, all right, then. But please tell him, just a little one, if it isn't too much trouble. I don't want to stay here much longer. I don't like this place. It's all dark and stuffy. It's the kind of place Edith would be crazy about – that's all I can say about this place. I know I oughtn't to talk about your best friend, Fred, but that's a terrible woman. That woman is the louse of this world. It makes me feel just awful that you trust that woman, Fred. I hate to see anybody play you dirt. I'd hate to see you get hurt. That's what makes me feel so terrible. That's why I'm getting mascara all over my face. No, please don't, Fred. You mustn't hold my hand. It wouldn't be fair to Edith. We've got to play fair with the big louse. After all, she's your best friend, isn't she?

Honestly? Do you honestly mean it, Fred? Yes, but how could I help thinking so, when you're with her all the time – when you bring her here every night in the week? Really, only Thursday? Oh, I know – I know how those things are. You simply can't help it, when you get stuck with a person that way. Lord, I'm glad you realise what an awful thing that woman is. I was worried about it, Fred. It's because I'm your friend. Why, of course I am, darling. You know I am. Oh, that's just silly, Freddie. You've got heaps of friends. Only you'll never find a better friend than I am. No, I know that. I know I'll never find a better friend than you are to me. Just give me back my hand a second, till I get this damned mascara out of my eye.

Yes, I think we ought to, honey. I think we ought to have a little drink, on account of our being friends. Just a little one, because it's real Scotch, and we're real friends. After all, friends are the greatest things in the world, aren't they, Fred? Gee, it makes you feel good to know you have a friend. I feel great, don't you, dear? And you look great, too. I'm proud to have you for a friend. Do you realise, Fred, what a rare thing a friend is, when you think of all the terrible people there are in this world? Animals are much better than people. God, I love animals. That's what I like about you, Fred. You're so fond of animals.

Look, I'll tell you what let's do, after we've had just a little highball. Let's go out and pick up a lot of stray dogs. I never had enough dogs in my life, did you? We ought to have more dogs. And maybe there'd be some cats around, if we looked. And a horse, I've never had one single horse, Fred. Isn't that rotten? Not one single horse. Ah, I'd like a nice old cab-horse, Fred. Wouldn't you? I'd like to take care of it and comb its hair and everything. Ah, don't be stuffy about it, Fred, please don't. I need a horse, honestly I do. Wouldn't you like one? It would be so sweet and kind. Let's have a drink and then let's you and I go out and get a horsie, Freddie – just a little one, darling, just a little one.

The Homebody

There still are kindly things for me to know,
Who am afraid to dream, afraid to feel –
This little chair of scrubbed and sturdy deal,
This easy book, this fire, sedate and slow.
And I shall stay with them, nor cry the woe
Of wounds across my breast that do not heal;
Nor wish that Beauty drew a duller steel,
Since I am sworn to meet her as a foe.

It may be, when the devil's own time is done,
That I shall hear the dropping of the rain
At midnight, and lie quiet in my bed;
Or stretch and straighten to the yellow sun;
Or face the turning tree, and have no pain;
So shall I learn at last my heart is dead.

Partial Comfort

Whose love is given over-well
Shall look on Helen's face in hell,
Whilst they whose love is thin and wise
May view John Knox in paradise.

Second Love

'So surely is she mine,' you say, and turn
Your quick and steady mind to harder things –
To bills and bonds and talk of what men earn –
And whistle up the stair, of evenings.
And do you see a dream behind my eyes,
Or ask a simple question twice of me –
'Thus women are,' you say; for men are wise
And tolerant, in their security.

How shall I count the midnights I have known
When calm you turn to me, nor feel me start,
To find my easy lips upon your own
And know my breast beneath your rhythmic heart.
Your god defer the day I tell you this:
My lad, my lad, it is not you I kiss!

Superfluous Advice

Should they whisper false of you,
Never trouble to deny;
Should the words they say be true,
Weep and storm and swear they lie.

The Whistling Girl

Back of my back, they talk of me,
  Gabble and honk and hiss;
Let them batten, and let them be –
  Me, I can sing them this:

'Better to shiver beneath the stars,
  Head on a faithless breast,
Than peer at the night through rusted bars,
  And share an irksome rest.

'Better to see the dawn come up,
  Along of a trifling one,
Than set a steady man's cloth and cup
  And pray the day be done.

'Better be left by twenty dears
  Than lie in a loveless bed;
Better a loaf that's wet with tears
  Than cold, unsalted bread.'

Back of my back, they wag their chins,
  Whinny and bleat and sigh;
But better a heart a-bloom with sins
  Than hearts gone yellow and dry!

THE LITTLE HOURS

Now what's this? What's the object of all this darkness all over me? They haven't gone and buried me alive while my back was turned, have they? Ah, now would you think they'd do a thing like that! Oh, no, I know what it is. I'm awake. That's it. I've waked up in the middle of the night. Well, isn't that nice. Isn't that simply ideal. Twenty minutes past four, sharp, and here's Baby wide-eyed as a marigold. Look at this, will you? At the time when all decent people are just going to bed, I must wake up. There's no way things can ever come out even, under this system. This is as rank as injustice is ever likely to get. This is what brings about hatred and bloodshed, that's what *this* does.

Yes, and you want to know what got me into this mess? Going to bed at ten o'clock, that's what. That spells ruin. T-e-n-space-o-apostrophe-c-l-o-c-k: ruin. Early to bed, and you'll wish you were dead. Bed before eleven, nuts before seven. Bed before morning, sailors give warning. Ten o'clock, after a quiet evening of reading. Reading – there's an institution for you. Why, I'd turn on the light and read, right this minute, if reading weren't what contributed toward driving me here. I'll show it. God, the bitter misery that reading works in this world! Everybody knows that – everybody who *is* everybody. All the best minds have been off reading for years. Look at the swing La Rochefoucauld took at it. He said that if nobody had ever learned to read, very few people would be in love. There was a man for you, and that's what *he* thought of it. Good for you, La Rochefoucauld; nice going, boy. I wish I'd never learned to read. I wish I'd never learned to take off my clothes. Then I wouldn't have been caught in this jam at half-past four in the morning. If nobody had ever learned to undress, very few people would be in love. No, his is better. Oh, well, it's a man's world.

La Rochefoucauld, indeed, lying quiet as a mouse, and me tossing and turning here! This is no time to be getting all steamed up about La Rochefoucauld. It's only a question of minutes before I'm going to be pretty darned good and sick of La Rochefoucauld, once and for all. La Rochefoucauld this and La

Rochefoucauld that. Yes, well, let me tell you that if nobody had ever learned to quote, very few people would be in love with La Rochefoucauld. I bet you I don't know ten souls who read him without a middleman. People pick up those scholarly little essays that start off 'Was it not that lovable old cynic, La Rochefoucauld, who said . . . ' and then they go around claiming to know the master backwards. Pack of illiterates, that's all they are. All right, let them keep their La Rochefoucauld, and see if I care. I'll stick to La Fontaine. Only I'd be better company if I could quit thinking that La Fontaine married Alfred Lunt.

I don't know what I'm doing mucking about with a lot of French authors at this hour, anyway. First thing you know, I'll be reciting *Fleurs du mal* to myself, and then I'll be little more good to anybody. And I'll stay off Verlaine too; he was always chasing Rimbauds. A person would be better off with La Rochefoucauld, even. Oh, damn La Rochefoucauld. The big Frog. I'll thank him to keep out of my head. What's he doing there, anyhow? What's La Rochefoucauld to me, or he to Hecuba? Why, I don't even know the man's first name, that's how close I ever was to *him*. What am I supposed to be, a hostess to La Rochefoucauld? That's what *he* thinks. Sez he. Well, he's only wasting his time, hanging around here. I can't help him. The only other thing I can remember his saying is that there is always something a little pleasing to us in the misfortunes of even our dearest friends. That cleans me all up with Monsieur La Rochefoucauld. *Maintenant c'est fini, ça.*

Dearest friends. A sweet lot of dearest friends *I've* got. All of them lying in swinish stupors, while I'm practically up and about. All of them stretched sodden through these, the fairest hours of the day, when man should be at his most productive. Produce, produce, produce, for I tell you the night is coming. Carlyle said that. Yes, and a fine one *he* was, to go shooting off his face on production. O Thomas Car*li*-yill, what *I* know about *you*-oo! No, that will be enough of that. I'm not going to start fretting about Carlyle, at this stage of the game. What did he ever do that was so great, besides founding a college for Indians? (That one ought to make him spin.) Let him keep his face out of this, if he knows what's good for him. I've got enough trouble with that lovable old cynic, La Rochefoucauld – him and the misfortunes of his dearest friends!

The first thing I've got to do is to get out and whip me up a complete new set of dearest friends; that's the first thing. Everything else can wait. And will somebody please kindly be so good as to inform me how I am ever going to meet up with any new people when my entire scheme of living is out of joint – when I'm the only living being awake while the rest of the world lies sleeping? I've got to get this thing adjusted. I must try to get back to sleep right now. I've got to conform to the rotten little standards of this sluggard civilisation. People needn't feel that they have to change their ruinous habits and come my way. Oh, no, no; no, indeed. Not at all. I'll go theirs. If that isn't the woman of it for you! Always having to do what somebody else wants, like it or not. Never able to murmur a suggestion of her own.

And what suggestion has anyone to murmur as to how I am going to drift lightly back to slumber? Here I am, awake as high noon what with all this milling and pitching around with La Rochefoucauld. I really can't be expected to drop everything and start counting sheep, at my age. I hate sheep. Untender it may be in me, but all my life I've hated sheep. It amounts to a phobia, the way I hate them. I can tell the minute there's one in the room. They needn't think that I am going to lie here in the dark and count their unpleasant little faces for them; I wouldn't do it if I didn't fall asleep again until the middle of next August. Suppose they never get counted – what's the worst that can happen? If the number of imaginary sheep in this world remains a matter of guesswork, who is richer or poorer for it? No, sir; *I'm* not their scorekeeper. Let them count themselves, if they're so crazy mad after mathematics. Let them do their own dirty work. Coming around here, at this time of day, and asking me to count them! And not even *real* sheep, at that. Why, it's the most preposterous thing I ever heard in my life.

But there must be *something* I could count. Let's see. No, I already know by heart how many fingers I have. I could count my bills, I suppose. I could count the things I didn't do yesterday

HOTEL
ASTOR
FOUR ROSES
LOEWS STATE
PLANTERS
VAUDEVILLE

that I should have done. I could count the things I should do today that I'm not going to do. I'm never going to accomplish anything; that's perfectly clear to me. I'm never going to be famous. My name will never be writ large on the roster of Those Who Do Things. I don't do anything. Not one single thing. I used to bite my nails, but I don't even do that any more. I don't amount to the powder to blow me to hell. I've turned out to be nothing but a bit of flotsam. Flotsam and leave 'em – that's me from now on. Oh, it's all terrible.

Well. This way lies galloping melancholia. Maybe it's because this is the zero hour. This is the time the swooning soul hangs pendant and vertiginous between the new day and the old, nor dares confront the one or summon back the other. This is the time when all things, known and hidden, are iron to weight the spirit; when all ways, travelled or virgin, fall away from the stumbling feet, when all before the straining eyes is black. Blackness now, everywhere is blackness. This is the time of abomination, the dreadful hour of the victorious dark. For it is always darkest – Was it not that lovable old cynic, La Rochefoucauld, who said it is always darkest before the deluge?

There. Now you see, don't you? Here we are again, practically back where we started. La Rochefoucauld, we are here. Ah, come on, son – how about your going your way and letting me go mine? I've got my work cut out for me right here; I've got all this sleeping to do. Think how I am going to look by daylight if this keeps up. I'll be a seamy sight for all those rested, clear-eyed, fresh-faced dearest friends of mine – the rats! My *dear*, whatever have you been doing; I thought you were so good lately. Oh, I was helling around with La Rochefoucauld till all hours; we couldn't stop laughing about your misfortunes. No, this is getting too thick, really. It isn't right to have this happen to a person, just because she went to bed at ten o'clock once in her life. Honest, I won't ever do it again. I'll go straight, after this. I'll never go to bed again, if I can only sleep now. If I can tear my mind away from a certain French cynic, *circa* 1650, and slip into lovely oblivion. 1650. I bet I look as if I'd been awake since then.

How do people go to sleep? I'm afraid I've lost the knack. I might try busting myself smartly over the temple with the night-light. I might repeat to myself, slowly and soothingly, a list of quotations beautiful from minds profound; if I can remember any of the damn things. That might do it. And it ought effectually to bar that visiting foreigner that's been hanging around ever since twenty minutes past four. Yes, that's what I'll do. Only wait till I turn the pillow; it feels as if La Rochefoucauld had crawled inside the slip.

Now let's see – where shall we start? Why – er – let's see. Oh, yes, I know one. This above all, to thine own self be true and it must follow, as the night the day, thou canst not then be false to any man. Now they're off. And once they get started, they ought to come like hot cakes. Let's see. Ah, what avail the sceptred race and what the form divine, when every virtue, every grace, Rose Aylmer, all were thine. Let's see. They also serve who only stand and wait. If Winter comes, can Spring be far behind? Lilies that fester smell far worse than weeds. Silent upon a peak in Darien. Mrs Porter and her daughter wash their feet in soda-water. And Agatha's Arth is a hug-the-hearth, but my true love is false. Why did you die when lambs were cropping, you should have died when apples were dropping. Shall be together, breathe and ride, so one day more am I deified, who knows but the world will end tonight. And he shall hear the stroke of eight and not the stroke of nine. They are not long, the weeping and the laughter; love and desire and hate I think will have no portion in us after we pass the gate. But none, I think, do there embrace. I think that I shall never see a poem lovely as a tree. I think I will not hang myself today. Ay tank Ay go home now.

Let's see. Solitude is the safeguard of mediocrity and the stern companion of genius. Consistency is the hobgoblin of little minds. Something is emotion remembered in tranquillity. A cynic is one who knows the price of everything and the value of nothing. That lovable old cynic is one who – oops, there's King Charles's head again. I've got to watch myself. Let's see. Circumstantial evidence is a trout in the milk. Any stigma will do to beat a dogma. If you would learn what God thinks about money, you have only to look at those to whom He has given it. If nobody had ever learned to read, very few people —

All right. That fixes it. I throw in the towel right now. I know when I'm licked. There'll be no more of this nonsense; I'm going to turn on the light and read my head off. Till the next ten o'clock, if I feel like it. And what does La Rochefoucauld want to make of that? Oh, he *will*, eh? Yes, he will! He and who else? La Rochefoucauld and *what* very few people?

For a Favourite Granddaughter

Never love a simple lad,
 Guard against a wise,
Shun a timid youth and sad,
 Hide from haunted eyes.

Never hold your heart in pain
 For an evil-doer;
Never flip it down the lane
 To a gifted wooer.

Never love a loving son,
 Nor a sheep astray;
Gather up your skirts and run
 From a tender way.

Never give away a tear,
 Never toss and pine;
Should you heed my words, my dear,
 You're no blood of mine!

Theory

Into love and out again,
 Thus I went, and thus I go.
Spare your voice, and hold your pen –
 Well and bitterly I know
All the songs were ever sung,
 All the words were ever said;
Could it be, when I was young,
 Someone dropped me on my head?

Vers Démodé

For one, the amaryllis and the rose;
  The poppy, sweet as never lilies are;
The ripen'd vine, that beckons as it blows;
  The dancing star.

For one, the trodden rosemary and rue;
  The bowl, dipt ever in the purple stream.
And, for the other one, a fairer due –
  Sleep, and no dream.

From a Letter from Lesbia

. . . So, praise the gods, Catullus is away!
  And let me tend you this advice, my dear:
Take any lover that you will, or may,
  Except a poet. All of them are queer.

It's just the same – a quarrel or a kiss
  Is but a tune to play upon his pipe.
He's always hymning that or wailing this;
  Myself, I much prefer the business type.

That thing he wrote, the time the sparrow died –
  (Oh, most unpleasant – gloomy, tedious words!)
I called it sweet, and made believe I cried;
  The stupid fool! I've always hated birds . . .

News Item

Men seldom make passes
At girls who wear glasses.

HORSIE

When young Mrs Gerald Cruger came home from the hospital, Miss Wilmarth came along with her and the baby. Miss Wilmarth was an admirable trained nurse, sure and calm and tireless, with a real taste for the arranging of flowers in bowls and vases. She had never known a patient to receive so many flowers, or such uncommon ones; yellow violets and strange lilies and little white orchids poised like a bevy of delicate moths along green branches. Care and thought must have been put into their selection that they, like all the other fragile and costly things she kept about her, should be so right for young Mrs Cruger. No one who knew her could have caught up the telephone and lightly bidden the florist to deliver to her one of his five-dollar assortments of tulips, stocks, and daffodils. Camilla Cruger was no complement to garden blooms.

Sometimes, when Miss Wilmarth opened the shiny boxes and carefully grouped the cards, there would come a curious expression upon her face. Playing over shorter features, it might almost have been one of wistfulness. Upon Miss Wilmarth, it served to perfect the strange resemblance that she bore through her years; her face was truly complete with that look of friendly melancholy peculiar to the gentle horse. It was not, of course, Miss Wilmarth's fault that she looked like a horse. Indeed, there was nowhere to attach any blame. But the resemblance remained.

She was tall, pronounced of bone, and erect of carriage; it was somehow impossible to speculate upon her appearance undressed. Her long face was innocent, indeed ignorant, of cosmetics, and its colour stayed steady. Confusion, heat, or haste caused her neck to flush crimson. Her mild hair was pinned with loops of nicked black wire into a narrow knot, practical to support her little high cap, like a charlotte russe from a bake-shop. She had big, trustworthy hands, scrubbed and dry, with nails cut short and so deeply cleaned with some small sharp instrument that the ends stood away from the spatulate fingertips. Gerald Cruger, who nightly sat opposite her at his own dinner-table, tried not to see her hands. It irritated him to be reminded by their sight that they must feel like straw matting and smell of white soap. For him, women who were not softly lovely were simply not women.

He tried, too, so far as it was possible to his beautiful manners, to keep his eyes from her face. Not that it was unpleasant – a kind face, certainly. But, as he told Camilla, once he looked he stayed fascinated, awaiting the toss and the whinny.

'I love horses, myself,' he said to Camilla, who lay all white and languid on her apricot satin chaise-longue. 'I'm a fool for a horse. Ah, what a noble animal, darling! All I say is, nobody has any business to go around looking like a horse and behaving as if it were all right. You don't catch horses going around looking like people, do you?'

He did not dislike Miss Wilmarth; he only resented her. He had no bad wish in the world for her, but he waited with longing the day she would leave. She was so skilled and rhythmic in her work that she disrupted the household but little. Nevertheless, her presence was an onus. There was that thing of dining with her every evening. It was a chore for him, certainly, and one that did not ease with repetition, but there was no choice. Everyone had always heard of trained nurses' bristling insistence that they be not treated as servants; Miss Wilmarth could not be asked to dine with the maids. He would not have dinner out; be away from *Camilla*? It was too much to expect the maids to institute a second dinner service or to carry trays, other than Camilla's, up and down the stairs. There were only three servants and they had work enough.

'Those children,' Camilla's mother was wont to say, chuckling. 'Those two kids. The independence of them! Struggling along on cheese and kisses. Why, they hardly let me pay for the trained nurse. And it was all we could do, last Christmas, to make Camilla take the Packard and the chauffeur.'

So Gerald dined each night with Miss Wilmarth. The small dread of his hour with her struck suddenly at him in the afternoon. He would forget it for stretches of minutes, only to be smitten sharper as the time drew near. On his way home from his office, he found grim entertainment in rehearsing his table talk, and plotting desperate innovations to it.

Cruger's Compulsory Conversations: Lesson I, a Dinner with a Miss Wilmarth, a Trained Nurse. Good evening, Miss Wilmarth. Well! And how were the patients all day? That's good, that's fine. Well! The baby gained two ounces, did she? That's fine. Yes, that's right, she will be before we know it. That's right. Well! Mrs Cruger seems to be getting stronger every day, doesn't she? That's good, that's fine. That's right, up and about before we know it. Yes, she certainly will. Well! Any visitors today? That's good. Didn't stay too long, did they? That's fine. Well! No, no, no, Miss Wilmarth – *you* go ahead. I wasn't going to say anything at all, really. No, really. Well! Well! I see where they found those two aviators after all. Yes, they certainly do run risks. That's right. Yes. Well! I see where they've been having a regular old-fashioned blizzard out west. Yes, we certainly have had a mild winter. That's right. Well! I see where they held up that jeweller's shop right in broad daylight on Fifth Avenue. Yes, I certainly don't know what we're coming to. That's right. Well! I see the cat. Do you see the cat? The cat is on the mat. It certainly is. Well! Pardon me, Miss Wilmarth, but must you look so much like a horse? Do you like to look like a horse, Miss Wilmarth? That's good, Miss Wilmarth, that's fine. You certainly do, Miss Wilmarth. That's right. Well! Will you for God's sake finish your oats, Miss Wilmarth, and let me get out of this?

Every evening he reached the dining-room before Miss Wilmarth and stared gloomily at silver and candle-flame until she was upon him. No sound of footfall heralded her coming, for her ample canvas Oxfords were soled with rubber; there would be a protest of parquet, a trembling of ornaments, a creak, a rustle, and the authoritative smell of stiff linen; and there she would be, set for her ritual of evening cheer.

'Well, Mary,' she would cry to the waitress, 'you know what they say – better late than never!'

But no smile would mellow Mary's lips, no light her eyes. Mary, in converse with the cook, habitually referred to Miss Wilmarth as 'that one'. She wished no truck with Miss

Wilmarth or any of the others of her guild; always in and out of a person's pantry.

Once or twice Gerald saw a strange expression upon Miss Wilmarth's face as she witnessed the failure of her adage with the maid. He could not quite classify it. Though he did not know, it was the look she sometimes had when she opened the shiny white boxes and lifted the exquisite, scentless blossoms that were sent to Camilla. Anyway, whatever it was, it increased her equine resemblance to such a point that he thought of proffering her an apple.

But she always had her big smile turned toward him when she sat down. Then she would look at the thick watch strapped to her wrist and give a little squeal that brought the edges of his teeth together.

'Mercy!' she would say. 'My good mercy! Why, I had no more idea it was so late. Well you mustn't blame me, Mr Cruger. Don't you scold *me*. You'll just have to blame that daughter of yours. She's the one that keeps us all busy.'

'She certainly is,' he would say. 'That's right.'

He would think, and with small pleasure, of the infant Diane, pink and undistinguished and angry, among the ruffles and *choux* of her bassinet. It was her doing that Camilla had stayed so long away from him in the odorous limbo of the hospital, her doing that Camilla lay all day upon her apricot satin chaise-longue. 'We must take our time,' the doctor said, 'just ta-a-ake our ti-yem.' Yes; well, that would all be because of young Diane. It was because of her, indeed, that night upon night he must face Miss Wilmarth and comb up conversation. All right, young Diane, there you are and nothing to do about it. But you'll be an only child, young woman, that's what you'll be.

Always Miss Wilmarth followed her opening pleasantry about the baby with a companion piece. Gerald had come to know it so well he could have said it in duet with her.

'You wait,' she would say. 'Just you wait. You're the one that's going to be kept busy when the beaux start coming around. You'll see. That young lady's going to be a heart-breaker if ever I saw one.'

'I guess that's right,' Gerald would say, and he would essay a small laugh and fail at it. It made him uncomfortable, somehow embarrassed him to hear Miss Wilmarth banter of swains and conquest. It was unseemly, as rouge would have been unseemly on her long mouth and perfume on her flat bosom.

He would hurry her over to her own ground. 'Well!' he would say. 'Well! And how were the patients all day?'

But that, even with the baby's weight and the list of the day's visitors, seldom lasted past the soup.

'Doesn't that woman ever go out?' he asked Camilla. 'Doesn't our Horsie ever rate a night off?'

'Where would she want to go?' Camilla said. Her low, lazy words had always the trick of seeming a little weary of their subject.

'Well,' Gerald said, 'she might take herself a moonlight canter around the park.'

'Oh, she doubtless gets a thrill out of dining with you,' Camilla said. 'You're a man, they tell me, and she can't have seen many. Poor old horse. She's not a bad soul.'

'Yes,' he said. 'And what a round of pleasure it is, having dinner every night with Not a Bad Soul.'

'What makes you think', Camilla said, 'that I am caught up in any whirl of gaiety, lying here?'

'Oh, darling,' he said. 'Oh, my poor darling. I didn't mean it, honestly I didn't. Oh, *Lord*, I didn't mean it. How could I complain, after all you've been through, and haven't I done a thing? Please, sweet, please. Ah, Camilla, say you know I didn't mean it.'

'After all,' Camilla said, 'you just have her at dinner. I have her around all day.'

'Sweetheart, please,' he said. 'Oh, poor angel.'

He dropped to his knees by the chaise-longue and crushed her limp, fragrant hand against his mouth. Then he remembered about being very, very gentle. He ran little apologetic kisses up and down her fingers and murmured of gardenias and lilies and thus exhausted his knowledge of white flowers.

Her visitors said that Camilla looked lovelier than ever,

but they were mistaken. She was only as lovely as she had always been. They spoke in hushed voices of the new look in her eyes since her motherhood; but it was the same far brightness that had always lain there. They said how white she was and how lifted above other people; they forgot that she had always been pale as moonlight and had always worn a delicate disdain, as light as the lace that covered her breast. Her doctor cautioned tenderly against hurry, besought her to take recovery slowly – Camilla, who had never done anything quickly in her life. Her friends gathered, adoring, about the apricot satin chaise-longue where Camilla lay and moved her hands as if they hung heavy from her wrists; they had been wont before to gather and adore at the white satin sofa in the drawing-room where Camilla reclined, her hands like heavy lilies in a languid breeze. Every night, when Gerald crossed the threshold of her fragrant room, his heart leaped and his words caught in his throat; but those things had always befallen him at the sight of her. Motherhood had not brought perfection to Camilla's loveliness. She had had that before.

Gerald came home early enough, each evening, to have a while with her before dinner. He made his cocktails in her room, and watched her as she slowly drank one. Miss Wilmarth was in and out, touching flowers, patting pillows. Sometimes she brought Diane in on display, and those would be minutes of real discomfort for Gerald. He could not bear to watch her with the baby in her arms, so acute was his vicarious embarrassment at her behaviour. She would bring her long head down close to Diane's tiny, stern face and toss it back again high on her rangy neck, all the while that strange words, in a strange high voice, came from her.

'Well, her wuzza booful dirl. Ess, her wuzza. Her wuzza, wuzza, wuzza. Ess, her *wuzz*.' She would bring the baby over to him. 'See, Daddy. Isn't us a gate, bid dirl? Isn't us booful? Say "nigh-nigh", Daddy. Us doe teepy-bye, now. Say "nigh-nigh".'

Oh, God.

Then she would bring the baby to Camilla. 'Say "nigh-nigh",' she would cry. '"Nigh-nigh", Mummy.'

'If that brat ever calls you "Mummy",' he told Camilla once, fiercely, 'I'll turn her out in the snow.'

Camilla would look at the baby, amusement in her slow glance. 'Good-night, useless,' she would say. She would hold out a finger, for Diane's pink hand to curl around. And Gerald's heart would quicken, and his eyes sting and shine.

Once he tore his gaze from Camilla to look at Miss Wilmarth, surprised by the sudden cessation of her falsetto. She was no longer lowering her head and tossing it back. She was standing quite still, looking at him over the baby; she looked away quickly, but not before he had seen that curious expression on her face again. It puzzled him, made him vaguely uneasy. That night, she made no further exhortations to Diane's parents to utter the phrase 'nigh-nigh'. In silence she carried the baby out of the room and back to the nursery.

One evening, Gerald brought two men home with him; lean, easily dressed young men, good at golf and squash rackets, his companions through his college and in his clubs. They had cocktails in Camilla's room, grouped about the chaise-longue. Miss Wilmarth, standing in the nursery adjoining, testing the temperature of the baby's milk against her wrist, could hear them all talking lightly and swiftly, tossing their sentences into the air to hang there unfinished. Now and again she could distinguish Camilla's lazy voice; the others stopped immediately when she spoke, and when she was done there were long peals of laughter. Miss Wilmarth pictured her lying there, in golden chiffon and deep lace, her light figure turned always a little away from those about her, so that she must move her head and speak her slow words over her shoulder to them. The trained nurse's face was astoundingly equine as she looked at the wall that separated them.

They stayed in Camilla's room a long time, and there was always more laughter. The door from the nursery into the hall was open, and presently she heard the door of Camilla's room being opened, too. She had been able to hear only voices before, but now she could distinguish Gerald's words as he called back from the threshold; they had no meaning to her.

'Only wait, fellers,' he said. 'Wait till you see Seabiscuit.'

He came to the nursery door. He held a cocktail shaker in one hand and a filled glass in the other.

'Oh, Miss Wilmarth,' he said. 'Oh, good evening, Miss Wilmarth. Why, I didn't know this door was open – I mean, I hope we haven't been disturbing you.'

'Oh, not the least little bit,' she said. 'Goodness.'

'Well!' he said. 'I – we were wondering if you wouldn't have a little cocktail. Won't you please?' He held out the glass to her.

'Mercy,' she said, taking it. 'Why, thank you ever so much. Thank you, Mr Cruger.'

'And, oh, Miss Wilmarth,' he said, 'would you tell Mary there'll be two more to dinner? And ask her not to have it before half an hour or so, will you? Would you mind?'

'Not the least little bit,' she said. 'Of course I will.'

'Thank you,' he said. 'Well! Thank you, Miss Wilmarth. Well! See you at dinner.'

'Thank *you*,' she said. 'I'm the one that ought to thank *you*. For the lovely little cockytail.'

'Oh,' he said, and failed at an easy laugh. He went back into Camilla's room and closed the door behind him.

Miss Wilmarth set her cocktail upon a table, and went down to inform Mary of the impending guests. She felt light and quick, and she told Mary gaily, awaiting a flash of gaiety in response. But Mary received the news impassively, made a grunt but no words, and slammed out through the swinging doors into the kitchen. Miss Wilmarth stood looking after her. Somehow servants never seemed to – She should have become used to it.

Even though the dinner hour was delayed, Miss Wilmarth was a little late. The three young men were standing in the dining-room, talking all at once and laughing all together. They stopped their noise when Miss Wilmarth entered, and Gerald moved forward to perform introductions. He looked at her, and then looked away. Prickling embarrassment tormented him. He introduced the young men, with his eyes away from her.

Miss Wilmarth had dressed for dinner. She had discarded

her linen uniform and put on a frock of dark blue taffeta, cut down to a point at the neck and given sleeves that left bare the angles of her elbows. Small, stiff ruffles occurred about the hips, and the skirt was short for its year. It revealed that Miss Wilmarth had clothed her ankles in roughened grey silk and her feet in black, casket-shaped slippers, upon which little bows quivered as if in lonely terror at the expanse before them. She had been busied with her hair; it was crimped and loosened, and ends that had escaped the tongs were already sliding from their pins. All the length of her nose and chin was heavily powdered; not with a perfumed dust, tinted to praise her skin, but with coarse, bright white talcum.

Gerald presented his guests; Miss Wilmarth, Mr Minot; Miss Wilmarth, Mr Forster. One of the young men, it turned out, was Freddy, and one, Tommy. Miss Wilmarth said she was pleased to meet each of them. Each of them asked her how she did.

She sat down at the candle-lit table with the three beautiful young men. Her usual evening vivacity was gone from her. In silence she unfolded her napkin and took up her soup spoon. Her neck glowed crimson, and her face, even with its powder, looked more than ever as if it should have been resting over the top rail of a paddock fence.

'Well!' Gerald said.

'Well!' Mr Minot said.

'Getting much warmer out, isn't it?' Mr Forster said. 'Notice it?'

'It is, at that,' Gerald said. 'Well. We're about due for warm weather.'

'Yes, we ought to expect it now,' Mr Minot said. 'Any day now.'

'Oh, it'll be here,' Mr Forster said. 'It'll come.'

'I love spring,' said Miss Wilmarth. 'I just love it.'

Gerald looked deep into his soup plate. The two young men looked at her.

'Darn good time of year,' Mr Minot said. 'Certainly is.'

'And how it is!' Mr Forster said.

They ate their soup.

There was champagne all through dinner. Miss Wilmarth watched Mary fill her glass, none too full. The wine looked gay and pretty. She looked about the table before she took her first sip. She remembered Camilla's voice and the men's laughter.

'Well,' she cried. 'Here's a health, everybody!'

The guests looked at her. Gerald reached for his glass and gazed at it as intently as if he beheld a champagne goblet for the first time. They all murmured and drank.

'Well!' Mr Minot said. 'Your patients seem to be getting along pretty well, Miss Witmark. Don't they?'

'I should say they do,' she said. 'And they're pretty nice patients, too. Aren't they, Mr Cruger?'

'They certainly are,' Gerald said. 'That's right.'

'They certainly are,' Mr Minot said. 'That's what they are. Well. You must meet all sorts of people in your work, I suppose. Must be pretty interesting.'

'Oh, sometimes it is,' Miss Wilmarth said. 'It depends on the people.' Her words fell from her lips clear and separate, sterile as if each had been freshly swabbed with boracic acid solution. In her ears rang Camilla's light, insolent drawl.

'That's right,' Mr Forster said. 'Everything depends on the people, doesn't it? Always does, wherever you go. No matter what you do. Still, it must be wonderfully interesting work. Wonderfully.'

'Wonderful the way this country's come right up in medicine,' Mr Minot said. 'They tell me we have the greatest doctors in the world, right here. As good as any in Europe. Or Harley Street.'

'I see', Gerald said, 'where they think they've found a new cure for spinal meningitis.'

'*Have* they really?' Mr Minot said.

'Yes, I saw that, too,' Mr Forster said. 'Wonderful thing. Wonderfully interesting.'

'Oh, say, Gerald,' Mr Minot said, and he went from there into an account, hole by hole, of his most recent performance at golf. Gerald and Mr Forster listened and questioned him.

The three young men left the topic of golf and came back to it again, and left it and came back. In the intervals, they related to Miss Wilmarth various brief items that had caught their eyes in the newspapers. Miss Wilmarth answered in exclamations, and turned her big smile readily to each of them. There was no laughter during dinner.

It was a short meal, as courses went. After it, Miss Wilmarth bade the guests good-night and received their bows and their '*Good*-night, Miss Witmark.' She said she was awfully glad to have met them. They murmured.

'Well, good-night, then, Mr Cruger,' she said. 'See you tomorrow!'

'Good-night, Miss Wilmarth,' Gerald said.

The three young men went and sat with Camilla. Miss Wilmarth could hear their voices and their laughter as she hung up her dark blue taffeta dress.

Miss Wilmarth stayed with the Crugers for five weeks. Camilla was pronounced well – so well that she could have dined downstairs on the last few nights of Miss Wilmarth's stay, had she been able to support the fardel of dinner at the table with the trained nurse.

'I really couldn't dine opposite that face,' she told Gerald. 'You go amuse Horsie at dinner, stupid. You must be good at it, by now.'

'All right, I will, darling,' he said. 'But God keep me, when she asks for another lump of sugar, from holding it out to her on my palm.'

'Only two more nights,' Camilla said, 'and then Thursday Nana'll be here, and she'll be gone forever.'

'"Forever", sweet, is my favourite word in the language,' Gerald said.

Nana was the round and competent Scottish woman who had nursed Camilla through her childhood and was scheduled to engineer the unknowing Diane through hers. She was a comfortable woman, easy to have in the house; a servant, and knew it.

Only two more nights. Gerald went down to dinner whistling a good old tune.

'The old grey mare, she ain't what she used to be,
Ain't what she used to be, ain't what she used to be — '

The final dinners with Miss Wilmarth were like all the others. He arrived first, and stared at the candles until she came.

'Well, Mary,' she cried on her entrance, 'you know what they say – better late than never.'

Mary, to the last, remained unamused.

Gerald was elated all the day of Miss Wilmarth's departure. He had a holiday feeling, a last-day-of-school jubilation with none of its faint regret. He left his office early, stopped at a florist's shop, and went home to Camilla.

Nana was installed in the nursery, but Miss Wilmarth had not yet left. She was in Camilla's room, and he saw her for the second time out of uniform. She wore a long brown coat and a brown rubbed velvet hat of no definite shape. Obviously, she was in the middle of the embarrassments of farewell. The melancholy of her face made it so like a horse's that the hat above it was preposterous.

'Why, there's Mr Cruger!' she cried.

'Oh, good evening, Miss Wilmarth,' he said. 'Well! Ah, hello, darling. How are you, sweet? Like these?'

He laid a florist's box in Camilla's lap. In it were strange little yellow roses, with stems and leaves and tiny, soft thorns all of blood red. Miss Wilmarth gave a little squeal at the sight of them.

'Oh, the darlings!' she cried. 'Oh, the boo-fuls!'

'And these are for you, Miss Wilmarth,' he said. He made himself face her and hold out to her a square, smaller box.

'Why, Mr Cruger,' she said. 'For me, really? Why, really, Mr Cruger.'

She opened the box and found four gardenias, with green foil and pale green ribbon holding them together.

'Oh, now, really, Mr Cruger,' she said. 'Why, I never in all my life – Oh, now, you shouldn't have done it. Really, you shouldn't. My good mercy! Well, I never saw anything so lovely in all my life. Did you, Mrs Cruger? They're *lovely*. Well, I just don't know how to *begin* to thank you. Why, I just – well, I just adore them.'

Gerald made sounds designed to convey the intelligence that he was glad she liked them, that it was nothing, that she was welcome. Her squeaks of thanks made red rise back of his ears.

'They're nice ones,' Camilla said. 'Put them on, Miss Wilmarth. And these are awfully cunning, Jerry. Sometimes you have your points.'

'Oh, I didn't think I'd *wear* them,' Miss Wilmarth said. 'I thought I'd just take them in the box like this, so they'd keep better. And it's such a nice box – I'd like to have it. I – I'd like to keep it.'

She looked down at the flowers. Gerald was in sudden horror that she might bring her head down close to them and toss it back high, crying 'wuzza wuzza, wuzza' at them the while.

'Honestly,' she said, 'I just can't take my eyes *off* them.'

'The woman is mad,' Camilla said. 'It's the effect of living with us, I suppose. I hope we haven't ruined you for life, Miss Wilmarth.'

'Why, Mrs Cruger,' Miss Wilmarth cried. 'Now, really! I was just telling Mrs Cruger, Mr Cruger, that I've never been on a pleasanter case. I've just had the time of my life, all the time I was here. I don't know when I – honestly, I can't stop looking at my posies, they're so lovely. Well, I just can't thank you for all you've done.'

'Well, we ought to thank you, Miss Wilmarth,' Gerald said. 'We certainly ought.'

'I really hate to say "goodbye",' Miss Wilmarth said. 'I just hate it.'

'Oh, don't say it,' Camilla said. 'I never dream of saying it. And remember, you must come in and see the baby, any time you can.'

'Yes, you certainly must,' Gerald said. 'That's right.'

'Oh, I will,' Miss Wilmarth said. 'Mercy, I just don't dare go take another look at her, or I wouldn't be able to leave, ever. Well, what am I thinking of! Why, the car's been waiting all this time. Mrs Cruger simply insists on sending me home in the car, Mr Cruger. Isn't she terrible?'

'Why, not at all,' he said. 'Why, of course.'

'Well, it's only five blocks down and over to Lexington,' she said, 'or I really couldn't think of troubling you.'

'Why, not at all,' Gerald said. 'Well! Is that where you live, Miss Wilmarth?'

She lived in some place of her own sometimes? She wasn't always disarranging somebody else's household?

'Yes,' Miss Wilmarth said. 'I have Mother there.'

Oh. Now Gerald had never thought of her having a mother. Then there must have been a father, too, sometime. And Miss Wilmarth existed because two people once had loved and known. It was not a thought to dwell upon.

'My aunt's with us, too,' Miss Wilmarth said. 'It makes it nice for Mother – you see, Mother doesn't get around very well any more. It's a little bit crowded for the three of us – I sleep on the davenport when I'm home, between cases. But it's so nice for Mother, having my aunt there.'

Even in her leisure, then, Miss Wilmarth was a disruption and a crowd. Never dwelling in a room that had been planned only for her occupancy; no bed, no corner of her own; dressing before other people's mirrors, touching other people's silver, never looking out one window that was hers. Well, doubtless she had known nothing else for so long that she did not mind or even ponder.

'Oh, yes,' Gerald said. 'Yes, it certainly must be fine for your mother. Well! Well! May I close your bags for you, Miss Wilmarth?'

'Oh, that's all done,' she said. 'The suitcase is downstairs. I'll just go get my hat-box. Well, goodbye, then, Mrs Cruger, and take care of yourself. And thank you a thousand times.'

'Good luck, Miss Wilmarth,' Camilla said. 'Come see the baby.'

Miss Wilmarth looked at Camilla and at Gerald standing beside her, touching one long white hand. She left the room to fetch her hat-box.

'I'll take it down for you, Miss Wilmarth,' Gerald called after her.

He bent and kissed Camilla gently, very, very gently.

'Well, it's nearly over, darling,' he said. 'Sometimes I am practically convinced that there is a God.'

'It was darn decent of you to bring her gardenias,' Camilla said. 'What made you think of it?'

'I was so crazed at the idea that she was really going', he said, 'that I must have lost my head. No one was more surprised than I, buying gardenias for Horsie. Thank the Lord she didn't put them on. I couldn't have stood that sight.'

'She's not really at her best in her street clothes,' Camilla said. 'She seems to lack a certain *chic*.' She stretched her arms slowly above her head and let them sink slowly back. 'That was a fascinating glimpse of her home life she gave us. Great fun.'

'Oh, I don't suppose she minds,' he said. 'I'll go down now and back her into the car, and that'll finish it.'

He bent again over Camilla.

'Oh, you look so lovely, sweet,' he said. 'So *lovely*.'

Miss Wilmarth was coming down the hall, when Gerald left the room, managing a pasteboard hat-box, the florist's box, and a big leather purse that had known service. He took the boxes from her, against her protests, and followed her down the stairs and out to the motor at the kerb. The chauffeur stood at the open door. Gerald was glad of that presence.

'Well, good luck, Miss Wilmarth,' he said. 'And thank you so much.'

'Thank *you*, Mr Cruger,' she said. 'I – I can't tell you how I've enjoyed it all the time I was here. I never had a pleasanter – And the flowers, and everything. I just don't know what to say. I'm the one that ought to thank *you*.'

She held out her hand, in a brown cotton glove. Anyway, worn cotton was easier to the touch than dry, corded flesh. It was the last moment of her. He scarcely minded looking at the long face on the red, red neck.

'Well!' he said. 'Well! Got everything? Well, good luck, again, Miss Wilmarth, and don't forget us.'

'Oh, I won't,' she said. 'I – oh, I won't do that.'

She turned from him and got quickly into the car, to sit upright against the pale grey cushions. The chauffeur placed her hat-box at her feet and the florist's box on the seat beside her, closed the door smartly, and returned to his wheel. Gerald waved cheerily as the car slid away. Miss Wilmarth did not wave to him.

When she looked back, through the little rear window, he had already disappeared in the house. He must have run across the sidewalk – run, to get back to the fragrant room and the little yellow roses and Camilla. Their little pink baby would lie sleeping in its bed. They would be alone together; they would dine alone together by candlelight; they would be alone together in the night. Every morning and every evening Gerald would drop to his knees beside her to kiss her perfumed hand and call her sweet. Always she would be perfect, in scented chiffon and deep lace. There would be lean, easy young men, to listen to her drawl and give her their laughter. Every day there would be shiny white boxes for her, filled with curious blooms. It was perhaps fortunate that no one looked in the limousine. A beholder must have been startled to learn that a human face could look as much like that of a weary mare as did Miss Wilmarth's.

Presently the car swerved, in a turn of the traffic. The florist's box slipped against Miss Wilmarth's knee. She looked down at it. Then she took it on her lap, raised the lid a little and peeped at the waxy white bouquet. It would have been all fair then for a chance spectator; Miss Wilmarth's strange resemblance was not apparent, as she looked at her flowers. They were her flowers. A man had given them to her. She had been given flowers. They might not fade maybe for days. And she could keep the box.

Garden-spot

God's acre was her garden-spot, she said;
  She sat there often, of the Summer days,
Little and slim and sweet, among the dead,
  Her hair a fable in the levelled rays.

She turned the fading wreath, the rusted cross,
  And knelt to coax about the wiry stem.
I see her gentle fingers on the moss
  Now it is anguish to remember them.

And once I saw her weeping, when she rose
  And walked away and turned to look around –
The quick and envious tears of one that knows
  She shall not lie in consecrated ground.

Sonnet for the End of a Sequence

So take my vows and scatter them to sea;
Who swears the sweetest is no more than human.
And say no kinder words than these of me:
'Ever she longed for peace, but was a woman!
And thus they are, whose silly female dust
Needs little enough to clutter it and bind it,
Who meet a slanted gaze, and ever must
Go build themselves a soul to dwell behind it.'

For now I am my own again, my friend!
This scar but points the whiteness of my breast;
This frenzy, like its betters, spins an end,
And now I am my own. And that is best.
Therefore, I am immeasurably grateful
To you, for proving shallow, false, and hateful.

The Flaw in Paganism

Drink and dance and laugh and lie,
Love, the reeling midnight through,
For tomorrow we shall die!
(But, alas, we never do.)

Transition

Too long and quickly have I lived to vow
The woe that stretches me shall never wane,
Too often seen the end of endless pain
To swear that peace no more shall cool my brow.
I know, I know – again the shrivelled bough
Will burgeon sweetly in the gentle rain,
And these hard lands be quivering with grain –
I tell you only: it is Winter now.

What if I know, before the Summer goes
Where dwelt this bitter frenzy shall be rest?
What is it now, that June shall surely bring
New promise, with the swallow and the rose?
My heart is water, that I first must breast
The terrible, slow loveliness of Spring.

Résumé

Razors pain you;
Rivers are damp;
Acids stain you;
And drugs cause cramp.
Guns aren't lawful;
Nooses give;
Gas smells awful;
You might as well live.

NEW YORK TO DETROIT

'All ready with Detroit,' said the telephone operator.

'Hello,' said the girl in New York.

'Hello?' said the young man in Detroit.

'O Jack!' she said. 'O darling, it's so wonderful to hear you. You don't know how much I — '

'Hello?' he said.

'Ah, can't you hear me?' she said. 'Why, I can hear you just as if you were right beside me. Is this any better, dear? Can you hear me now?'

'Who did you want to speak to?' he said.

'You, Jack!' she said. 'You, you. This is Jean, darling. Oh, please try to hear me. This is Jean.'

'Who?' he said.

'Jean,' she said. 'Ah, don't you know my voice? It's Jean, dear. Jean.'

'Oh, hello there,' he said. 'Well. Well, for Heaven's sake. How are you?'

'I'm all right,' she said. 'Oh, I'm not, either, darling. I – oh, it's just terrible. I can't stand it any more. Aren't you coming back? Please, when are you coming back? You don't know how awful it is, without you. It's been such a long time, dear – you said it would be just four or five days, and it's nearly three weeks. It's like years and years. Oh, it's been so awful, sweetheart – it's just — '

'Hey, I'm terribly sorry,' he said, 'but I can't hear one damn thing you're saying. Can't you talk louder, or something?'

'I'll try, I'll try,' she said. 'Is this better? Now can you hear?'

'Yeah, now I can, a little,' he said. 'Don't talk so fast, will you? What did you say, before?'

'I said it's just awful without you,' she said. 'It's such a long time, dear. And I haven't had a word from you. I – oh, I've just been nearly crazy, Jack. Never even a postcard, dearest, or a — '

'Honestly, I haven't had a second,' he said. 'I've been working like a fool. God, I've been rushed.'

'Ah, have you?' she said. 'I'm sorry, dear. I've been silly.

But it was just – oh, it was just hell, never hearing a word. I thought maybe you'd telephone to say good-night, sometimes – you know, the way you used to, when you were away.'

'Why, I was going to, a lot of times,' he said, 'but I thought you'd probably be out, or something.'

'I haven't been out,' she said. 'I've been staying here, all by myself. It's – it's sort of better, that way. I don't want to see people. Everybody says, "When's Jack coming back?" and "What do you hear from Jack?" and I'm afraid I'll cry in front of them. Darling, it hurts so terribly when they ask me about you, and I have to say I don't —'

'This is the damnedest, lousiest connection I ever saw in my life,' he said. 'What hurts? What's the matter?'

'I said, it hurts so terribly when people ask me about you,' she said, 'and I have to say – Oh, never mind. Never mind. How are you, dear? Tell me how you are.'

'Oh, pretty good,' he said. 'Tired as the devil. You all right?'

'Jack, I – that's what I wanted to tell you,' she said. 'I'm terribly worried. I'm nearly out of my mind. Oh, what will I do, dear, what are we going to do? Oh, Jack, Jack, darling!'

'Hey, how can I hear you when you mumble like that?' he said. 'Can't you talk louder? Talk right into the what-you-call-it.'

'I can't scream it over the telephone!' she said. 'Haven't you any sense? Don't you know what I'm telling you? Don't you know? Don't you know?'

'I give up,' he said. 'First you mumble, and then you yell. Look, this doesn't make sense. I can't hear anything, with this rotten connection. Why don't you write me a letter, in the morning? Do that, why don't you? And I'll write you one. See?'

'Jack, listen, listen!' she said. 'You listen to me! I've got to talk to you. I tell you I'm nearly crazy. Please, dearest, hear what I'm saying. Jack, I — '

'Just a minute,' he said. 'Someone's knocking at the door. *Come in. Well, for cryin' out loud! Come on in, bums. Hang your coats up on the floor, and sit down. The Scotch is in the closet, and there's ice in that pitcher. Make yourselves at home – act like you were in a regular bar. Be with you right away*. Hey, listen, there's a lot of crazy Indians just come in here, and I can't hear myself think. You go ahead and write me a letter tomorrow. Will you?'

'Write you a letter!' she said. 'O God, don't you think I'd have written you before, if I'd known where to reach you? I didn't even know that, till they told me at your office today. I got so — '

'Oh, yeah, did they?' he said. 'I thought I – *Ah, pipe down, will you? Give a guy a chance. This is an expensive talk going on here*. Say, look, this must be costing you a million dollars. You oughtn't to do this.'

'What do you think I care about that?' she said. 'I'll die if I don't talk to you. I tell you I'll die, Jack. Sweetheart, what is it? Don't you want to talk to me? Tell me what makes you this way. Is it – don't you really like me any more? Is that it? Don't you, Jack?'

'Hell, I can't hear,' he said. 'Don't what?'

'Please,' she said. 'Please, please. Please, Jack, listen. When are you coming back, darling? I need you so. I need you so terribly. When are you coming back?'

'Why, that's the thing,' he said. 'That's what I was going to write you about tomorrow. *Come on, now, how about shutting up just for a minute? A joke's a joke*. Hello. Hear me all right? Why, you see, the way things came out today, it looks a little bit like I'd have to go on to Chicago for a while. Looks like a pretty big thing, and it won't mean a very long time, I don't believe. Looks as if I'd be going out there next week, I guess.'

'Jack, no!' she said. 'Oh, don't do that! You can't do that. You can't leave me alone like this. I've got to see you, dearest. I've got to. You've got to come back, or I've got to come there to you. I can't go through this. Jack, I can't, I — '

'Look, we better say good-night now,' he said. 'No use trying to make out what you say, when you talk all over yourself like that. And there's so much racket here – *Hey, can the harmony, will you? God, it's terrible. Want me to be thrown out of here?* You go get a good night's sleep, and I'll write you all about it tomorrow.'

'Listen!' she said. 'Jack, don't go 'way! Help me, darling. Say something to help me through tonight. Say you love me, for God's sake say you still love me. Say it. Say it.'

'Ah, I can't talk,' he said. 'This is fierce. I'll write you first thing in the morning. 'Bye. Thanks for calling up.'

'Jack!' she said. 'Jack, don't go. Jack, wait a minute. I've got to talk to you. I'll talk quietly. I won't cry. I'll talk so you can hear me. Please, dear, please — '

'All through with Detroit?' said the operator.

'No!' she said. 'No, no, no! Get him, get him back again right away! Get him back. No, never mind. Never mind it now. Never — '

Purposely Ungrammatical Love Song

There's many and many, and not so far,
  Is willing to dry my tears away;
There's many to tell me what you are,
  And never a lie to all they say.

It's little the good to hide my head,
  It's never the use to bar my door;
There's many as counts the tears I shed,
  There's mourning hearts for my heart is sore.

There's honester eyes than your blue eyes,
  There's better a mile than such as you.
But when did I say that I was wise,
  And when did I hope that you were true!

General Review of the Sex Situation

Woman wants monogamy;
Man delights in novelty.
Love is woman's moon and sun;
Man has other forms of fun.
Woman lives but in her lord;
Count to ten, and man is bored.
With this the gist and sum of it,
What earthly good can come of it?

Ultimatum

I'm wearied of wearying love, my friend,
   Of worry and strain and doubt;
Before we begin, let us view the end,
   And maybe I'll do without.
There's never the pang that was worth the tear,
   And toss in the night I won't –
So either you do or you don't, my dear,
   Either you do or you don't!

The table is ready, so lay your cards
   And if they should augur pain,
I'll tender you ever my kind regards
   And run for the fastest train.
I haven't the will to be spent and sad;
   My heart's to be gay and true –
Then either you don't or you do, my lad,
   Either you don't or you do!

Summary

Every love's the love before
   In a duller dress.
That's the measure of my lore –
   Here's my bitterness:
Would I knew a little more,
   Or very much less!

Requiescat

Tonight my love is sleeping cold
  Where none may see and none shall pass.
The daisies quicken in the mould,
  And richer fares the meadow grass.

The warding cypress pleads the skies,
  The mound goes level in the rain.
My love all cold and silent lies –
  Pray God it will not rise again!

Social Note

Lady, lady, should you meet
One whose ways are all discreet,
One who murmurs that his wife
Is the lodestar of his life,
One who keeps assuring you
That he never was untrue,
Never loved another one . . .
Lady, lady, better run!

FROM THE DIARY OF A NEW YORK LADY

During Days of Horror, Despair, and World Change

Monday. Breakfast tray about eleven; didn't want it. The champagne at the Amorys' last night was *too* revolting, but what *can* you do? You can't stay until five o'clock on just *nothing*. They had those *divine* Hungarian musicians in the green coats, and Stewie Hunter took off one of his shoes and led them with it, and it *couldn't* have been funnier. He is *the* wittiest number in the *entire* world; he *couldn't* be more perfect. Ollie Martin brought me home and we both fell asleep in the car – *too* screaming. Miss Rose came about noon to do my nails, simply *covered* with *the* most divine gossip. The Morrises are going to separate *any minute*, and Freddie Warren *definitely* has ulcers, and Gertie Leonard simply *won't* let Bill Crawford out of her sight even with Jack Leonard *right there in the room*, and it's all *true* about Sheila Phillips and Babs Deering. It *couldn't* have been more thrilling. Miss Rose is *too* marvellous; I really think that a lot of times people like that are a lot more intelligent than a lot of people. Didn't notice until after she had gone that the damn fool had put that *revolting* tangerine-coloured polish on my nails; *couldn't* have been more furious. Started to read a book, but too nervous. Called up and found I could get two tickets for the opening of *Run like a Rabbit* tonight for forty-eight dollars. Told them they had *the* nerve of the world, but what *can* you do? Think Joe said he was dining out, so telephoned some *divine* numbers to get someone to go to the theatre with me, but they were all tied up. Finally got Ollie Martin. He *couldn't* have more poise, and what do *I* care if he *is* one? *Can't* decide whether to wear the green crêpe or the red wool. Every time I look at my finger-nails, I could *spit*. *Damn* Miss Rose.

Tuesday. Joe came barging in my room this morning at *practically nine o'clock*. *Couldn't* have been more furious. Started to fight, but *too* dead. Know he said he wouldn't be home to dinner. Absolutely *cold* all day; couldn't *move*. Last night *couldn't* have been more perfect. Ollie and I dined at Thirty-Eight East, absolutely *poisonous* food, and not one *living* soul that you'd be seen *dead* with, and *Run like a Rabbit* was *the* world's worst. Took Ollie up to the Barlows' party and it *couldn't* have been more attractive – *couldn't* have been more people absolutely *stinking.* They had those Hungarians in the green coats, and Stewie Hunter was leading them with a fork – everybody simply *died.* He had *yards* of green toilet paper hung around his neck like a lei; he *couldn't* have been in better form. Met a *really new number*, very tall, *too* marvellous, and one of those people that you can *really* talk to them. I told him sometimes I get so *nauseated* I could *yip*, and I felt I absolutely *had* to do something like write or paint. He said why didn't I write or paint. Came home alone; Ollie passed out *stiff*. Called up the new number three times today to get him to come to dinner and go with me to the opening of *Never Say Good Morning*, but first he was out and then he was all tied up with his mother. Finally got Ollie Martin. Tried to read a book, but couldn't sit still. *Can't* decide whether to wear the red lace or the pink with the feathers. Feel *too* exhausted, but what *can* you do?

Wednesday. The most terrible thing happened *just this minute.* Broke one of my finger-nails *right off short.* Absolutely *the* most horrible thing I ever had happen to me in my life. Called up Miss Rose to come over and shape it for me, but she was out for the day. I do have *the* worst luck in the *entire* world. Now I'll have to go around like this all day and all night, but what *can* you do? *Damn* Miss Rose. Last night *too* hectic. *Never Say Good Morning too* foul, *never* saw more poisonous clothes on the stage. Took Ollie up to the Ballards' party; *couldn't* have been better. They had those Hungarians in the green coats and Stewie Hunter was leading them with a freesia – *too* perfect. He had on Peggy Cooper's ermine coat and Phyllis Minton's silver turban; *simply* unbelievable. Asked simply *sheaves of divine* people to come here Friday night; got the address of those Hungarians in the green coats from Betty Ballard. She says just engage them until four, and then whoever gives them another three hundred

Dad ho Slew Daughter
Tried Suicide May
eat Justice by Death
Joseph Ungerman, 50, who killed his daughter last night, may escape in death the grim accounting of the law. If he lives, the middle-aged man who ran amuck will face not only a charge of murder, but the accusations of the parents of a 13-year-old girl.
EVENING GRAPHIC
Wise Featu
WHITE SH
for Over the
LYLE
MARCELLA
WHITE KI
THEO
JOCASTA

dollars, they'll stay till five. *Couldn't* be cheaper. Started home with Ollie, but had to drop him at his house; he *couldn't* have been sicker. Called up the new number today to get him to come up to dinner and go to the opening of *Everybody Up* with me tonight, but he was tied up. Joe's going to be out; he didn't *condescend* to say *where, of course.* Started to read the papers, but nothing in them except that Mona Wheatley is in Reno charging *intolerable cruelty*. Called up Jim Wheatley to see if he had anything to do tonight, but he was tied up. Finally got Ollie Martin. *Can't* decide whether to wear the white satin or the black chiffon or the yellow pebble crêpe. Simply *wrecked* to the *core* about my finger-nail. Can't *bear* it. *Never* knew *anybody* to have such *unbelievable* things happen to them.

Thursday. Simply *collapsing* on my *feet*. Last night *too* marvellous. *Everybody Up too* divine, *couldn't* be filthier, and the new number was there, *too* celestial, only he didn't see me. He was with Florence Keeler in that *loathsome* gold Schiaparelli model of hers that every *shopgirl* has had since *God* knows. He must be out of his *mind*; she wouldn't *look* at a man. Took Ollie to the Watsons' party; *couldn't* have been more thrilling. Everybody simply *blind*. They had those Hungarians in the green coats and Stewie Hunter was leading them with a lamp, and, after the lamp got broken, he and Tommy Thomas did adagio dances – *too* wonderful. Somebody told me Tommy's doctor told him he had to absolutely get *right out of town*, he has *the* world's worst stomach, but you'd *never* know it. Came home alone, couldn't find Ollie *anywhere*. Miss Rose came at noon to shape my nail, *couldn't* have been more fascinating. Sylvia Eaton can't go *out the door* unless she's had a hypodermic, and Doris Mason *knows every single word* about Douggie Mason and that girl up in Harlem, and Evelyn North won't be *induced* to keep away from those three acrobats, and they don't *dare* tell Stuyvie Raymond *what* he's got the matter with him. *Never* knew anyone that had a more simply *fascinating* life than Miss Rose. Made her take that *vile* tangerine polish off my nails and put on dark red. Didn't notice until after she had gone that it's practically *black* in electric light; *couldn't* be in a worse state. *Damn* Miss Rose. Joe left a note saying he was going out to dine, so telephoned the new number to get him to come to dinner and go with me to that new movie tonight, but he didn't answer. Sent him three telegrams to *absolutely surely* come tomorrow night. Finally got Ollie Martin for tonight. Looked at the papers, but nothing in them except that the Harry Motts are throwing a tea with Hungarian music on Sunday. Think will ask the new number to go to it with me; they must have meant to invite me. Began to read a book, but too exhausted. *Can't* decide whether to wear the new blue with the white jacket or save it till tomorrow night and wear the ivory moire. Simply *heartsick* every time I think of my nails. *Couldn't* be wilder. Could *kill* Miss Rose, but what *can* you do?

Friday. Absolutely *sunk; couldn't* be worse. Last night *too* divine, movie *simply* deadly. Took Ollie to the Kingslands' party, *too* unbelievable, everybody absolutely *rolling*. They had those Hungarians in the green coats, but Stewie Hunter wasn't there. He's got a *complete* nervous breakdown. Worried *sick* for fear he won't be well by tonight; will absolutely *never* forgive him if he doesn't come. Started home with Ollie, but dropped him at his house because he *couldn't* stop crying. Joe left word with the butler he's going to the country this afternoon for the weekend; of *course* he wouldn't *stoop* to say *what* country. Called up *streams* of marvellous numbers to get someone to come dine and go with me to the opening of *White Man's Folly*, and then go somewhere after to dance for a while; can't *bear* to be the first one there at your own party. Everybody was tied up. Finally got Ollie Martin. *Couldn't* feel more depressed; never should have gone *anywhere* near champagne and Scotch together. Started to read a book, but too restless. Called up Anne Lyman to ask about the new baby and *couldn't* remember if it was a boy or girl – *must* get a secretary *next week*. Anne *couldn't* have been more of a help; she said she didn't know whether to name it Patricia or Gloria, so then of course I knew it was a girl *right away*. Suggested calling it Barbara; forgot she already had one. Absolutely *walking the floor* like a *panther* all day. Could *spit* about Stewie Hunter. Can't *face* deciding whether to wear the blue with the white jacket or the purple with the beige roses. Every time I look at those *revolting* black nails, I want to absolutely *yip*. I really have *the* most horrible things happen to me of anybody in the *entire* world. *Damn* Miss Rose.

One Perfect Rose

A single flow'r he sent me, since we met.
   All tenderly his messenger he chose;
Deep-hearted, pure, with scented dew still wet –
   One perfect rose.

I knew the language of the floweret;
   'My fragile leaves', it said, 'his heart enclose.'
Love long has taken for his amulet
   One perfect rose.

Why is it no one ever sent me yet
   One perfect limousine, do you suppose?
Ah no, it's always just my luck to get
   One perfect rose.

Inventory

Four be the things I am wiser to know:
Idleness, sorrow, a friend, and a foe.

Four be the things I'd been better without:
Love, curiosity, freckles, and doubt.

Three be the things I shall never attain:
Envy, content, and sufficient champagne.

Three be the things I shall have till I die:
Laughter and hope and a sock in the eye.

Sonnet on an Alpine Night

My hand, a little raised, might press a star;
Where I may look, the frosted peaks are spun,
So shaped before Olympus was begun,
Spanned each to each, now, by a silver bar.
Thus to face Beauty have I travelled far,
But now, as if around my heart were run
Hard, lacing fingers, so I stand undone.
Of all my tears, the bitterest these are.

Who humbly followed Beauty all her ways,
Begging the brambles that her robe had passed,
Crying her name in corridors of stone,
That day shall know his weariedest of days –
When Beauty, still and suppliant at last,
Does not suffice him, once they are alone.

Words of Comfort to be Scratched on a Mirror

Helen of Troy had a wandering glance;
Sappho's restriction was only the sky;
Ninon was ever the chatter of France;
But oh, what a good girl am I!

SENTIMENT

Oh, anywhere, driver, anywhere – it doesn't matter. Just keep driving.

It's better here in this taxi than it was walking. It's no good my trying to walk. There is always a glimpse through the crowd of someone who looks like him – someone with his swing of the shoulders, his slant of the hat. And I think it's he, I think he's come back. And my heart goes to scalding water and the buildings sway and bend above me. No, it's better to be here. But I wish the driver would go fast, so fast that people walking by would be a long grey blur, and I could see no swinging shoulders, no slanted hat. It's bad stopping still in the traffic like this. People pass too slowly, too clearly, and always the next one might be – No, of course it couldn't be. I know that. Of course I know it. But it might be, it might.

And people can look in and see me, here. They can see if I cry. Oh, let them – it doesn't matter. Let them look and be damned to them.

Yes, you look at me. Look and look and look, you poor, queer tired woman. It's a pretty hat, isn't it? It's meant to be looked at. That's why it's so big and red and new, that's why it has these great soft poppies on it. Your poor hat is all weary and done with. It looks like a dead cat, a cat that was run over and pushed out of the way against the kerbstone. Don't you wish you were I and could have a new hat whenever you pleased? You could walk fast, couldn't you, and hold your head high and raise your feet from the pavement if you were on your way to a new hat, a beautiful hat, a hat that cost more than ever you had? Only I hope you wouldn't choose one like mine. For red is mourning, you know. Scarlet red for a love that's dead. Didn't you know that?

She's gone now. The taxi is moving and she's left behind forever. I wonder what she thought when our eyes and our lives met. I wonder did she envy me, so sleek and safe and young. Or did she realise how quick I'd be to fling away all I have if I could bear in my breast the still, dead heart that she carries in hers.

She doesn't feel. She doesn't even wish. She is done with hoping and burning, if ever she burned and she hoped. Oh, that's quite nice, it has a real lilt. She is done with hoping and burning, if ever she – Yes, it's pretty. Well – I wonder if she's gone her slow way a little happier, or, perhaps, a little sadder for knowing that there is one worse off than herself.

This is the sort of thing he hated so in me. I know what he would say. 'Oh, for Heaven's sake!' he would say. 'Can't you stop that fool sentimentalising? Why do you have to do it? Why do you *want* to do it? Just because you see an old charwoman on the street, there's no need to get sobbing about her. She's all right. She's fine. "When your eyes and your lives met" – oh, come on now. Why, she never even saw you. And her "still, dead heart", nothing! She's probably on her way to get a bottle of bad gin and have a roaring time. You don't have to dramatise *everything*. You don't have to insist that *everybody's* sad. Why are you always so sentimental? Don't *do* it, Rosalie.' That's what he would say. I know.

But he won't say that or anything else to me, any more. Never anything else, sweet or bitter. He's gone away and he isn't coming back. 'Oh, of course I'm coming back!' he said. 'No, I don't know just when – I told you that. Ah, Rosalie, don't go making a national tragedy of it. It'll be a few months, maybe – and if ever two people needed a holiday from each other! It's nothing to cry about. I'll be back. I'm not going to stay away from New York forever.'

But I knew. I knew. I knew because he had been far away from me long before he went. He's gone away and he won't come back. He's gone away and he won't come back, he's gone away and he'll never come back. Listen to the wheels saying it, on and on and on. That's sentimental, I suppose. Wheels don't say anything. Wheels can't speak. But I *hear* them.

I wonder why it's wrong to be sentimental. People are so contemptuous of feeling. 'You wouldn't catch *me* sitting alone and mooning,' they say. 'Moon' is what they say when they mean remember, and they are so proud of not remembering. It's strange, how they pride themselves upon their lacks. 'I never take anything seriously,' they say. 'I simply couldn't imagine', they say, 'letting myself care so much that I could be hurt.' They say, 'No one person could be that important to *me*.' And why, why do they think they're right?

Oh, who's right and who's wrong and who decides? Perhaps it was I who was right about that charwoman. Perhaps she *was* weary and still-hearted, and perhaps for just that moment, she knew all about me. She needn't have been all right and fine and on her way for gin, just because he said so. Oh. Oh, I forgot. He didn't say so. He wasn't here; he isn't here. It was I, imagining what he would say. And I thought I heard him. He's always with me, he and all his beauty and his cruelty. But he mustn't be any more. I mustn't think of him. That's it, don't think of him. Yes. Don't breathe, either. Don't hear. Don't see. Stop the blood in your veins.

I can't go on like this. I can't. I can't. I cannot stand this frantic misery. If I knew it would be over in a day or a year or two months, I could endure it. Even if it grew duller sometimes and wilder sometimes, it could be borne. But it is always the same and there is no end.

'Sorrow like a ceaseless rain
Beats upon my heart.
People twist and scream in pain –
Dawn will find them still again;
This has neither wax nor wane,
Neither stop nor start.'

Oh, let's see – how does the next verse go? Something, something, something, something, something to rhyme with 'wear'. Anyway, it ends:

'All my thoughts are slow and brown:
Standing up or sitting down
Little matters, or what gown
Or what shoes I wear.'

Yes, that's the way it goes. And it's right, it's so right. What is it to me what I wear? Go and buy yourself a big red hat with poppies on it – that ought to cheer you up. Yes – go buy it and loathe it. How am I to go on, sitting and staring and buying big red hats and hating them, and then sitting and staring again – day upon day upon day upon day? Tomorrow and tomorrow and tomorrow. How am I to drag through them like this?

But what else is there for me? 'Go out and see your friends and have a good time,' they say. 'Don't sit alone and dramatise yourself.' Dramatise yourself! If it be drama to feel a steady – no, a *ceaseless* rain beating upon my heart, then I do dramatise myself. The shallow people, the little people, how can they know what suffering is, how could their thick hearts be torn? Don't they know, the empty fools, that I could not see again the friends we saw together, could not go back to the places where he and I have been? For he's gone, and it's ended. It's ended, it's ended. And when it ends, only those places where you have known sorrow are kindly to you. If you revisit the scenes of your happiness, your heart must burst of its agony.

And that's sentimental, I suppose. It's sentimental to know that you cannot bear to see the places where once all was well with you, that you cannot bear reminders of a dead loveliness. Sorrow is tranquillity remembered in emotion. It – oh, I think that's quite good. 'Remembered in emotion' – that's a really nice reversal. I wish I could say it to him. But I won't say anything to him, ever again, ever, ever again. He's gone, and it's over, and I dare not think of the dead days. All my thoughts must be slow and brown, and I must —

Oh, no, no, no! Oh, the driver shouldn't go through this street! This was our street, this is the place of our love and our laughter. I can't do this, I can't, I can't. I will crouch down here, and hold my hands tight, tight over my eyes, so that I cannot look. I must keep my poor heart still, and I must be like the little, mean, dry-souled people who are proud not to remember.

But, oh, I see it, I see it, even though my eyes are blinded. Though I had no eyes, my heart would tell me this street, out of all streets. I know it as I know my hands, as I know his face. Oh, why can't I be let to die as we pass through?

We must be at the florist's shop on the corner now. That's where he used to stop to buy me primroses, little yellow primroses massed tight together with a circle of their silver-backed leaves about them, clean and cool and gentle. He always said that orchids and camellias were none of my affair. So when there were no spring and no primroses, he would give me lilies of the valley and little, gay rosebuds and mignonette and bright blue cornflowers. He said he couldn't stand the thought of me without flowers – it would be all wrong; I cannot bear flowers near me, now. And the little grey florist was so interested and so glad – and there was the day he called me 'madam'! Ah, I can't, I can't.

And now we must be at the big apartment house with the big gold doorman. And the evening the doorman was holding the darling puppy on a big, long leash, and we stopped to talk to it, and he took it up in his arms and cuddled it, and that was the only time we ever saw the doorman smile! And next is the house with the baby, and he always would take off his hat and bow very solemnly to her, and sometimes she would give him her little starfish of a hand. And then is the tree with the rusty iron bars around it, where he would stop to turn and wave to me, as I leaned out the window to watch him. And people would look at him, because people always had to look at him, but he never noticed. It was our tree, he said; it wouldn't dream of belonging to anybody else. And very few city people had their own personal tree, he said. Did I realise that, he said.

And then there's the doctor's house, and the three thin grey houses and then – oh, God, we must be at our house now! Our house, though we had only the top floor. And I loved the long, dark stairs, because he climbed them every evening. And our little prim pink curtains at the windows, and the boxes of pink geraniums that always grew for me. And the little stiff entry and the funny mail-box, and his ring at the bell. And I waiting for him in the dusk, thinking he would never come; and yet the waiting was lovely, too. And then when I opened the door to him – Oh, no, no, no! Oh, no one could bear this. No one, no one.

Ah, why, why, why must I be driven through here? What torture could there be so terrible as this? It will be better if I uncover my eyes and look. I will see our tree and our house again, and then my heart will burst and I will be dead. I will look, I will look.

But where's the tree? Can they have cut down our tree – *our* tree? And where's the apartment house? And where's the florist's shop? And where – oh, where's our house, where's —

Driver, what street is this? Sixty-Fifth? Oh, no, nothing, thank you. I – I thought it was Sixty-Third . . .

The Lady's Reward

Lady, lady, never start
Conversation toward your heart;
Keep your pretty words serene;
Never murmur what you mean.
Show yourself, by word and look,
Swift and shallow as a brook.
Be as cool and quick to go
As a drop of April snow;
Be as delicate and gay
As a cherry flower in May.
Lady, lady, never speak
Of the tears that burn your cheek –
She will never win him, whose
Words had shown she feared to lose.
Be you wise and never sad,
You will get your lovely lad.
Never serious be, nor true,
And your wish will come to you –
And if that makes you happy, kid,
You'll be the first it ever did.

War Song

Soldier, in a curious land
All across a swaying sea,
Take her smile and lift her hand –
Have no guilt of me.

Soldier, when were soldiers true?
If she's kind and sweet and gay,
Use the wish I send to you –
Lie not lone till day!

Only, for the nights that were,
Soldier, and the dawns that came,
When in sleep you turn to her
Call her by my name.

Thought for a Sunshiny Morning

It costs me never a stab nor squirm
To tread by chance upon a worm.
'Aha, my little dear,' I say,
'Your clan will pay me back one day.'

CLOTHE THE NAKED

Big Lannie went out by the day to the houses of secure and leisured ladies, to wash their silks and their linens. She did her work perfectly; some of the ladies even told her so. She was a great, slow mass of a woman, coloured a sound brown-black save for her palms and the flat of her fingers that were like gutta-percha from steam and hot suds. She was slow because of her size, and because the big veins in her legs hurt her, and her back ached much of the time. She neither cursed her ills nor sought remedies for them. They had happened to her; there they were.

Many things had happened to her. She had had children, and the children had died. So had her husband, who was a kind man, cheerful with the little luck he found. None of their children had died at birth. They had lived to be four or seven or ten, so that they had had their ways and their traits and their means of causing love; and Big Lannie's heart was always wide for love. One child had been killed in a street accident and two others had died of illnesses that might have been no more than tedious, had there been fresh food and clear spaces and clean air behind them. Only Arlene, the youngest, lived to grow up.

Arlene was a tall girl, not so dark as her mother but with the same firm flatness of colour. She was so thin that her bones seemed to march in advance of her body. Her little pipes of legs and her broad feet with jutting heels were like things a child draws with crayons. She carried her head low, her shoulders scooped around her chest, and her stomach slanted forward. From the time that she was tiny, there were men after her.

Arlene was a bad girl always; that was one of the things that happened to Big Lannie. There it was, and Big Lannie could only keep bringing her presents, surprises, so that the girl would love her mother and would want to stay at home. She brought little bottles of sharp perfume, and pale stockings of tinny silk, and rings set with bits of green and red glass; she tried to choose what Arlene would like. But each time Arlene came home she had bigger rings and softer stockings and stronger perfume than her mother could buy for her. Sometimes she would stay with her mother over a night, and sometimes more than a week; and then Big Lannie would come back from work one evening, and the girl would be gone, and no word of her. Big Lannie would go on bringing surprises, and setting them out along Arlene's bed to wait a return.

Big Lannie did not know it, when Arlene was going to have a baby. Arlene had not been home in nearly half a year; Big Lannie told the time in days. There was no news at all of the girl until the people at the hospital sent for Big Lannie to come to her daughter and grandson. She was there to hear Arlene say the baby must be named Raymond, and to see the girl die. For whom Raymond was called, or if anyone, Big Lannie never knew.

He was a long, light-coloured baby, with big milky eyes that looked right back at his grandmother. It was several days before the people at the hospital told her he was blind.

Big Lannie went to each of the ladies who employed her and explained that she could not work for some while; she must take care of her grandson. The ladies were sharply discommoded, after her steady years, but they dressed their outrage in shrugs and cool tones. Each arrived, separately, at the conclusion that she had been too good to Big Lannie, and had been imposed upon, therefore. 'Honestly, those niggers!' each said to her friends. 'They're all alike.'

Big Lannie sold most of the things she lived with, and took one room with a stove in it. There, as soon as the people at the hospital would let her, she brought Raymond and tended him. He was all her children to her.

She had always been a saving woman, with few needs and no cravings, and she had been long alone. Even after Arlene's burial, there was enough left for Raymond and Big Lannie to go on for a time. Big Lannie was slow to be afraid of what must come; fear did not visit her at all, at first, and then it slid in only when she waked, when the night hung motionless before another day.

Raymond was a good baby, a quiet, patient baby, lying in his wooden box and stretching out his delicate hands to the sounds that were light and colour to him. It seemed but a little while, so short to Big Lannie, before he was walking about the room, his hands held out, his feet quick and sure. Those of Big Lannie's friends who saw him for the first time had to be told that he could not see.

Then, and it seemed again such a little while, he could dress himself, and open the door for his granny, and unlace the shoes from her tired feet, and talk to her in his soft voice. She had occasional employment – now and then a neighbour would hear of a day's scrubbing she could do, or sometimes she might work in the stead of a friend who was sick – infrequent, and not to be planned on. She went to the ladies for whom she had worked, to ask if they might not want her back again; but there was little hope in her, after she had visited the first one. Well, now, really, said the ladies; well, really, now.

The neighbours across the hall watched over Raymond while Big Lannie looked for work. He was no trouble to them, nor to himself. He sat and crooned at his chosen task. He had been given a wooden spool around the top of which were driven little brads, and over these with a straightened hairpin he looped bright worsted, working faster than sight until a long tube of woven wool fell through the hole in the spool. The neighbours threaded big, blunt needles for him, and he coiled the woollen tubes and sewed them into mats. Big Lannie called them beautiful, and it made Raymond proud to have her tell him how readily she sold them. It was hard for her, when he was asleep at night, to unravel the mats and wash the worsted and stretch it so straight that even Raymond's shrewd fingers could not tell, when he worked with it next day, that it was not new.

Fear stormed in Big Lannie and took her days and nights. She might not go to any organisation dispensing relief, for dread that Raymond would be taken from her and put in – she would not say the word to herself, and she and her neighbours lowered their voices when they said it to one another – an institution. The neighbours wove lingering tales of what happened inside certain neat, square buildings on the cindery skirts of the town, and, if they must go near them, hurried as if passing graveyards, and came home heroes. When they got you in one of those places, whispered the neighbours, they laid your spine open with whips, and then when you dropped, they kicked your head in. Had anyone come into Big Lannie's room to take Raymond away to an asylum for the blind, the neighbours would have fought for him with stones and rails and boiling water.

Raymond did not know about anything but good. When he grew big enough to go alone down the stairs and into the street, he was certain of delight each day. He held his head high, as he came out into the little yard in front of the flimsy wooden house, and slowly turned his face from side to side, as if the air were soft liquid in which he bathed it. Trucks and wagons did not visit the street, which ended in a dump for rusted bedsprings and broken boilers and staved-in kettles; children played over its cobbles, and men and women sat talking in open windows and called across to one another in gay, rich voices. There was always laughter for Raymond to hear, and he would laugh back, and hold out his hands to it.

At first, the children stopped their play when he came out, and gathered quietly about him, and watched him, fascinated. They had been told of his affliction, and they had a sort of sickened pity for him. Some of them spoke to him, in soft, careful tones. Raymond would laugh with pleasure, and stretch his hands, the curious smooth, flat hands of the blind, to their voices. They would draw sharply back, afraid that his strange hands might touch them. Then, somehow ashamed because they had shrunk from him and he could not see that they had done so, they said gentle goodbyes to him, and backed away into the street again, watching him steadily.

When they were gone, Raymond would start on his walk to the end of the street. He guided himself by lightly touching the broken fences along the dirt sidewalk, and as he walked he crooned little songs with no words to them. Some of the men and women at the windows would call hello to him, and he would call back and wave and smile. When the children, forgetting him, laughed again at their games, he stopped and turned to the sound as if it were the sun.

In the evening, he would tell Big Lannie about his walk, slapping his knee and chuckling at the memory of the laughter he had heard. When the weather was too hard for him to go out in the street, he would sit at his worsted work, and talk all day of going out the next day.

The neighbours did what they could for Raymond and Big Lannie. They gave Raymond clothes their own children had not yet worn out, and they brought food, when they had enough to spare and other times. Big Lannie would get through a week, and would pray to get through the next one; and so the months went. Then the days on which she could find work fell further and further apart, and she could not pray about the time to come because she did not dare to think of it.

It was Mrs Ewing who saved Raymond's and Big Lannie's lives, and let them continue together. Big Lannie said that then and ever after; daily she blessed Mrs Ewing, and nightly she would have prayed for her, had she not known, in some dimmed way, that any intercession for Mrs Delabarre Ewing must be impudence.

Mrs Ewing was a personage in the town. When she went to Richmond for a visit, or when she returned from viewing the azalea gardens in Charleston, the newspaper always printed the fact. She was a woman rigorously conscious of her noble obligation; she was prominent on the Community Chest committee, and it was she who planned and engineered the annual Bridge Drive to raise funds for planting salvia around the cannon in front of the DAR headquarters. These and many others were her public activities, and she was no less exacting of herself in her private life. She kept a model, though childless, house for her husband and herself, relegating the supervision of details to no domestic lieutenant, no matter how seemingly trustworthy.

Back before Raymond was born, Big Lannie had worked as laundress for Mrs Ewing. Since those days, the Ewing wash tubs had witnessed many changes, none for the better. Mrs Ewing took Big Lannie back into her employment. She apologised for this step to her friends by the always winning method of self-deprecation. She knew she was a fool, she said, after all that time, and after the way that Big Lannie had treated her. But still, she said – and she laughed a little at her own ways – anyone she felt kind of sorry for could always get around her, she said. She knew it was awful foolish, but that, she said, was the way she was. Mr Ewing, she said behind her husband's hearing, always called her just a regular little old easy mark.

Big Lannie had no words in which to thank Mrs Ewing, nor to tell her what two days' assured employment every week could mean. At least, it was fairly assured. Big Lannie, as Mrs Ewing pointed out to her, had got no younger, and she had always been slow. Mrs Ewing kept her in a state of stimulating insecurity by referring, with perfect truth, to the numbers of stronger, quicker women who were also in need of work.

Two days' work in the week meant money for rent and stovewood and almost enough food for Raymond and Big Lannie. She must depend, for anything further, on whatever odd jobs she could find, and she must not stop seeking them. Pressed on by fear and gratitude, she worked so well for Mrs Ewing that there was sometimes expressed satisfaction at the condition of the lady's household linen and her own and her husband's clothing. Big Lannie had a glimpse of Mr Ewing occasionally, leaving the house as she came, or entering it as she was leaving. He was a bit of a man, not much bigger than Raymond.

Raymond grew so fast that he seemed to be taller each morning. Every day he had his walk in the street to look forward to and experience, and tell Big Lannie about at night. He had ceased to be a sight of the street; the children were so used to him that they did not even look at him, and the men and women at the windows no longer noticed him enough to hail him. He did not know. He would wave to any gay cry he heard, and go on his way, singing his little songs and turning toward the sound of laughter.

Then his lovely list of days ended as sharply as if ripped from some bright calendar. A winter came, so sudden and savage as to find no comparison in the town's memories, and Raymond had no clothes to wear out in the street. Big Lannie mended his out-grown garments as long as she could, but the stuff had so rotted with wear that it split in new places when she tried to sew together the ragged edges of rents.

The neighbours could give no longer; all they had they must keep for their own. A demented coloured man in a nearby town had killed the woman who employed him, and terror had spread like brush fire. There was a sort of panic of reprisal; coloured employees were dismissed from their positions, and there was no new work for them. But Mrs Ewing, admittedly soft-hearted certainly to a fault and possibly to a peril, kept her black laundress on. More than ever Big Lannie had reason to call her blessed.

All winter, Raymond stayed indoors. He sat at his spool and worsted, with Big Lannie's old sweater about his shoulders and, when his tattered knickerbockers would no longer hold together, a calico skirt of hers lapped around his waist. He lived, at his age, in the past; in the days when he had walked, proud and glad, in the street, with laughter in his ears. Always, when he talked of it, he must laugh back at that laughter.

Since he could remember, he had not been allowed to go out when Big Lannie thought the weather unfit. This he had accepted without question, and so he accepted his incarceration through the mean weeks of the winter. But then one day it was spring, so surely that he could tell it even in the smoky, stinking rooms of the house, and he cried out with joy because now he might walk in the street again. Big Lannie had to explain to him that his rags were too thin to shield him, and that there were no odd jobs for her, and so no clothes and shoes for him.

Raymond did not talk about the street any more, and his fingers were slow at his spool.

Big Lannie did something she had never done before; she begged of her employer. She asked Mrs Ewing to give her some of Mr Ewing's old clothes for Raymond. She looked at the floor and mumbled so that Mrs Ewing requested her to talk *up*. When Mrs Ewing understood, she was, she said, surprised. She had, she said, a great, great many demands on her charity, and she would have supposed that Big Lannie, of all people, might have known that she did everything she could, and, in fact, a good deal more.

She spoke of inches and ells. She said that if she found she could spare anything, Big Lannie was kindly to remember it was to be just for this once.

When Big Lannie was leaving at the end of her day's work, Mrs Ewing brought her a package with her own hands. There, she said, was a suit and a pair of shoes; beautiful, grand things that people would think she was just a crazy to go giving away like that. She simply didn't know, she said, what Mr Ewing would say to her for being such a crazy. She explained that that was the way she was when anyone got around her, all the while Big Lannie was trying to thank her.

Big Lannie had never before seen Raymond behave as he did when she brought him home the package. He jumped and danced and clapped his hands, he tried to speak and squealed instead, he tore off the paper himself, and ran his fingers over the close-woven cloth and held it to his face and kissed it. He put on the shoes and clattered about in them, digging with his toes and heels to keep them on; he made Big Lannie pin the trousers around his waist and roll them up over his shins. He babbled of the morrow when he would walk in the street, and could not say his words for laughing.

Big Lannie must work for Mrs Ewing the next day, and she had thought to bid Raymond wait until she could stay at home and dress him herself in his new garments. But she heard him laugh again; she could not tell him he must wait. He might go out at noon next day, she said, when the sun was so warm that he would not take cold at his first outing; one of the neighbours across the hall would help him with the clothes. Raymond chuckled and sang his little songs until he went to sleep.

After Big Lannie left in the morning, the neighbour came in to Raymond, bringing a pan of cold pork and corn bread for his lunch. She had a call for a half-day's work, and she could not stay to see him start out for his walk. She helped him put on the trousers and pinned and rolled them for him, and she laced the shoes as snug as they would go on his feet. Then she told him not to go out till the noon whistles blew, and kissed him, and left.

Raymond was too happy to be impatient. He sat and thought of the street and smiled and sang. Not until he heard the whistles did he go to the drawer where Big Lannie had laid the coat, and take it out and put it on. He felt it soft on his bare back, he twisted his shoulders to let it fall warm and loose from them. As he folded the sleeves back over his thin arms, his heart beat so that the cloth above it fluttered.

The stairs were difficult for him to manage, in the big shoes, but the very slowness of the descent was delicious to him. His anticipation was like honey in his mouth.

Then he came out into the yard, and turned his face in the gentle air. It was all good again; it was all given back again. As quickly as he could, he gained the walk and set forth, guiding himself by the fence. He could not wait; he called out, so that he would hear gay calls in return, he laughed so that laughter would answer him.

He heard it. He was so glad that he took his hand from the fence and turned and stretched out his arms and held up his smiling face to welcome it. He stood there, and his smile died on his face, and his welcoming arms stiffened and shook.

It was not the laughter he had known; it was not the laughter he had lived on. It was like great flails beating him flat, great prongs tearing his flesh from his bones. It was coming at him, to kill him. It drew slyly back, and then it smashed against him. It swirled around and over him, and he could not breathe. He screamed and tried to run out through it, and fell, and it licked over him, howling higher. His clothes unrolled, and his shoes flapped on his feet. Each time he could rise, he fell again. It was as if the street were perpendicular before him, and the laughter leaping at his back. He could not find the fence, he did not know which way he was turned. He lay screaming, in blood and dust and darkness.

When Big Lannie came home, she found him on the floor in a corner of the room, moaning and whimpering. He still wore his new clothes, cut and torn and dusty, and there was dried blood on his mouth and his palms. Her heart had leapt in alarm when he had not opened the door at her footstep, and she cried out so frantically to ask what had happened that she frightened him into wild weeping. She could not understand what he said; it was something about the street, and laughing at him, and make them go away, and don't let him go in the street no more, never in the street no more. She did not try to make him explain. She took him in her arms and rocked him, and told him, over and over, never mind, don't care, everything's all right. Neither he nor she believed her words.

But her voice was soft and her arm warm. Raymond's sobs softened, and trembled away. She held him, rocking silently and rhythmically, a long time. Then gently she set him on his feet, and took from his shoulders Mr Ewing's old full-dress coat.

Prayer for a New Mother

The things she knew, let her forget again –
  The voices in the sky, the fear, the cold,
The gaping shepherds, and the queer old men
  Piling their clumsy gifts of foreign gold.

Let her have laughter with her little one;
  Teach her the endless, tuneless songs to sing;
Grant her her right to whisper to her son
  The foolish names one dare not call a king.

Keep from her dreams the rumble of a crowd,
  The smell of rough-cut wood, the trail of red,
The thick and chilly whiteness of the shroud
  That wraps the strange new body of the dead.

Ah, let her go, kind Lord, where mothers go
  And boast his pretty words and ways, and plan
The proud and happy years that they shall know
  Together, when her son is grown a man.

The Heaven Times
BANNED!
Angel
Gabriel
in noise
rumpus

Tombstones in the Starlight

I The Minor Poet

His little trills and chirpings were his best.
No music like the nightingale's was born
Within his throat; but he, too, laid his breast
Upon a thorn.

II The Pretty Lady

She hated bleak and wintry things alone.
All that was warm and quick, she loved too well –
A light, a flame, a heart against her own;
It is forever bitter cold, in Hell.

III The Very Rich Man

He'd have the best, and that was none too good;
No barrier could hold, before his terms.
He lies below, correct in cypress wood,
And entertains the most exclusive worms.

IV The Fisherwoman

The man she had was kind and clean
And well enough for every day,
But, oh, dear friends, you should have seen
The one that got away!

V The Crusader

Arrived in Heaven, when his sands were run
He seized a quill, and sat him down to tell
The local press that something should be done
About that noisy nuisance, Gabriel.

VI The Actress

Her name, cut clear upon this marble cross,
Shines, as it shone when she was still on earth;
While tenderly the mild, agreeable moss
Obscures the figures of her date of birth.

For a Sad Lady

And let her loves, when she is dead,
  Write this about her bones:
'No more she lives to give us bread
  Who asked her only stones.'

Indian Summer

In youth, it was a way I had
  To do my best to please,
And change, with every passing lad,
  To suit his theories.

But now I know the things I know,
  And do the things I do;
And if you do not like me so,
  To hell, my love, with you!

Faute de Mieux

Travel, trouble, music, art,
  A kiss, a frock, a rhyme –
I never said they feed my heart,
  But still they pass my time.

THE LOVELY LEAVE

Her husband had telephoned her by long distance to tell her about the leave. She had not expected the call, and she had no words arranged. She threw away whole seconds explaining her surprise at hearing him, and reporting that it was raining hard in New York, and asking was it terribly hot where he was. He had stopped her to say, look, he didn't have time to talk long; and he had told her quickly that his squadron was to be moved to another field the next week and on the way he would have twenty-four hours' leave. It was difficult for her to hear. Behind his voice came a jagged chorus of young male voices, all crying the syllable 'Hey!'

'Ah, don't hang up yet,' she said. 'Please. Let's talk another minute, just another — '

'Honey, I've got to go,' he said. 'The boys all want a crack at the telephone. See you a week from today, around five. 'Bye.'

Then there had been a click as his receiver went back into place. Slowly she cradled her telephone, looking at it as if all frustrations and bewilderments and separations were its fault. Over it she had heard his voice, coming from far away. All the months, she had tried not to think of the great blank distance between them; and now that far voice made her know she had thought of nothing else. And his speech had been brisk and busy. And from back of him had come gay, wild young voices, voices he heard every day and she did not, voices of those who shared his new life. And he had heeded them and not her, when she begged for another minute. She took her hand off the telephone and held it away from her with the fingers spread stiffly apart, as if it had touched something horrid.

Then she told herself to stop her nonsense. If you looked for things to make you feel hurt and wretched and unnecessary, you were certain to find them, more easily each time, so easily, soon, that you did not even realise you had gone out searching. Women alone often developed into experts at the practice. She must never join their dismal league.

What was she dreary about, anyway? If he had only a little

while to talk, then he had only a little while to talk, that was all. Certainly he had had time to tell her he was coming, to say that they would be together soon. And there she was, sitting scowling at the telephone, the kind, faithful telephone that had brought her the lovely news. She would see him in a week. Only a week. She began to feel, along her back and through her middle, little quivers of excitement, like tiny springs uncoiling into spirals.

There must be no waste to this leave. She thought of the preposterous shyness that had fallen upon her when he had come home before. It was the first time she had seen him in uniform. There he stood, in their little apartment, a dashing stranger in strange, dashing garments. Until he had gone into the army, they had never spent a night apart in all their marriage; and when she saw him, she dropped her eyes and twisted her handkerchief and could bring nothing but monosyllables from her throat. There must be no such squandering of minutes this time. There must be no such gangling diffidence to lop even an instant from their twenty-four hours of perfect union. O Lord, only twenty-four hours . . .

No. That was exactly the wrong thing to do; that was directly the wrong way to think. That was the way she had spoiled it before. Almost as soon as the shyness had left her and she felt she knew him again, she had begun counting. She was so filled with the desperate consciousness of the hours sliding away – only twelve more, only five, O dear God, only one left – that she had no room for gaiety and ease. She had spent the golden time in grudging its going.

She had been so woebegone of carriage, so sad and slow of word as the last hour went, that he, nervous under the pall, had spoken sharply and there had been a quarrel. When he had had to leave for his train, there were no clinging farewells, no tender words to keep. He had gone to the door and opened it and stood with it against his shoulder while he shook out his flight cap and put it on, adjusting it with great care, one inch over the eye, one inch above the ear. She stood in the middle of the living-room, cool and silent, looking at him.

When his cap was precisely as it should be, he looked at her.

'Well,' he said. He cleared his throat. 'Guess I'd better get going.'

'I'm sure you had,' she said.

He studied his watch intently. 'I'll just make it,' he said.

'I'm sure you will,' she said.

She turned, not with an actual shrug, only with the effect of one, and went to the window and looked out, as if casually remarking the weather. She heard the door close loudly and then the grind of the elevator.

When she knew he was gone, she was cool and still no longer. She ran about the little flat, striking her breast and sobbing.

Then she had two months to ponder what had happened, to see how she had wrought the ugly small ruin. She cried in the nights.

She need not brood over it any more. She had her lesson; she could forget how she had learned it. This new leave would be the one to remember, the one he and she would have, to keep forever. She was to have a second chance, another twenty-four hours with him. After all, that is no short while, you know; that is, if you do not think of it as a thin little row of hours dropping off like beads from a broken string. Think of it as a whole long day and a whole long night, shining and sweet, and you will be all but overawed by your fortune. For how many people are there who have the memory of a whole long day and a whole long night, shining and sweet, to carry with them in their hearts until they die?

To keep something, you must take care of it. More, you must understand just what sort of care it requires. You must know the rules and abide by them. She could do that. She had been doing it all the months, in the writing of her letters to him. There had been rules to be learned in that matter, and the first of them was the hardest: never say to him what you want him to say to you. Never tell him how sadly you miss him, how it grows no better, how each day without him is sharper than the day before. Set down for him the gay happenings about you, bright little anecdotes, not invented, necessarily, but attractively embellished. Do not bedevil him with the pinings of your faithful heart because he is your husband, your man, your love. For you are writing to none of these. You are writing to a soldier.

She knew those rules. She would have said that she would rather die, and she would have meant something very near the words, than send a letter of complaint or sadness or cold anger to her husband, a soldier far away, strained and weary from his work, giving all he had for the mighty cause. If in her letters she could be all he wanted her to be, how much easier to be it when they were together. Letters were difficult; every word had to be considered and chosen. When they were together again, when they could see and hear and touch each other, there would be no stiltedness. They would talk and laugh together. They would have tenderness and excitement. It would be as if they had never been separated. Perhaps they never had been. Perhaps a strange new life and strange empty miles and strange gay voices had no existence for two who were really one.

She had thought it out. She had learned the laws of what not to do. Now she could give herself up to the ecstasy of waiting his coming.

It was a fine week. She counted the time again, but now it was sweet to see it go. Two days after tomorrow, day after tomorrow, tomorrow. She lay awake in the dark, but it was a thrilling wakefulness. She went tall and straight by day, in pride in her warrior. On the street, she looked with amused pity at women who walked with men in civilian suits.

She bought a new dress; black – he liked black dresses – simple – he liked plain dresses – and so expensive that she would not think of its price. She charged it, and realised that for months to come she would tear up the bill without removing it from its envelope. All right – this was no time to think of months to come.

The day of the leave was a Saturday. She flushed with gratitude to the army for this coincidence, for after one o'clock, Saturday was her own. She went from her office without stopping for lunch, and bought perfume and toilet water and bath oil. She had a bit of each remaining in bottles on her dressing-table and in her bathroom, but it made her feel desired and secure to have rich new stores of them. She bought a night-gown, a delightful thing of soft chiffon patterned with little bouquets, with innocent puffs of sleeves and a Romney neck and a blue sash. It could never withstand laundering, a French cleaner must care for it – all right. She hurried home with it, to fold it in a satin sachet.

Then she went out again and bought the materials for cocktails and whiskies-and-sodas, shuddering at their cost. She went a dozen blocks to buy the kind of salted biscuits he liked with drinks. On the way back she passed a florist's shop in the window of which were displayed potted fuchsia. She made no attempt to resist them. They were too charming, with their delicate parchment-coloured inverted cups and their graceful magenta bells. She bought six pots of them. Suppose she did without lunches the next week – all right.

When she was done with the little living-room, it looked gracious and gay. She ranged the pots of fuchsia along the window sill, she drew out a table and set it with glasses and bottles, she plumped the pillows and laid bright-covered magazines about invitingly. It was a place where someone entering eagerly would find delighted welcome.

Before she changed her dress, she telephoned downstairs to the man who tended both the switchboard and the elevator.

'Oh,' she said, when he eventually answered. 'Oh, I just want to say, when my husband, Lieutenant McVicker, comes, please send him right up.'

There was no necessity for the call. The wearied attendant would have brought up anyone to any flat without the additional stress of a telephoned announcement. But she wanted to say the words. She wanted to say 'my husband' and she wanted to say 'lieutenant'.

She sang, when she went into the bedroom to dress. She had a sweet, uncertain little voice that made the lusty song ludicrous.

'Off we go, into the wild blue yonder,
Climbing high into the sun, sun, sun, sun, sun.
Here they come; zooming to meet our thunder –
At 'em boys, give 'er the gun!'

She kept singing, in a preoccupied way, while she gave close attention to her lips and her eyelashes. Then she was silent and held her breath as she drew on the new dress. It was good to her. There was a reason for the cost of those perfectly plain black dresses. She stood looking at herself in the mirror with deep interest, as if she watched a chic unknown, the details of whose costume she sought to memorise.

As she stood there, the bell rang. It rang three times, loud and quick. He had come.

She gasped, and her hands fluttered over the dressing-table. She seized the perfume atomiser and sprayed scent violently all about her head and shoulders, some of it reaching them. She had already perfumed herself, but she wanted another minute, another moment, anything. For it had taken her again – the outrageous shyness. She could not bring herself to go to the door and open it. She stood, shaking, and squirted perfume.

The bell rang three times loud and quick again, and then an endless peal.

'Oh, *wait*, can't you?' she cried. She threw down the atomiser, looked wildly around the room as if for a hiding-place, then sternly made herself tall and sought to control the shaking of her body. The shrill noise of the bell seemed to fill the flat and crowd the air out of it.

She started for the door. Before she reached it, she stopped, held her hands over her face, and prayed. 'Oh, please let it be all right,' she whispered. 'Please keep me from doing wrong things. Please let it be lovely.'

Then she opened the door. The noise of the bell stopped. There he stood in the brightly lighted little hall. All the long sad nights, and all the strong and sensible vows. And now he had come. And there she stood.

'Well, for Heaven's sake!' she said. 'I had no idea there was anybody out here. Why, you were just as quiet as a little mouse.'

'Well! Don't you ever open the door?' he said.

'Can't a woman have time to put on her shoes?' she said.

He came in and closed the door behind him. 'Ah, darling,' he said. He put his arms around her. She slid her cheek along his lips, touched her forehead to his shoulder, and broke away from him.

'Well!' she said. 'Nice to see you, Lieutenant. How's the war?'

'How are you?' he said. 'You look wonderful.'

'Me?' she said. 'Look at you.'

He was well worth looking at. His fine clothes complemented his fine body. The precision of his appointments was absolute, yet he seemed to have no consciousness of it. He stood straight, and he moved with grace and assurance. His face was browned. It was thin, so thin that the bones showed under the cheeks and down the jaws; but there was no look of strain in it. It was smooth and serene and confident. He was the American officer, and there was no finer sight than he.

'Well!' she said. She made herself raise her eyes to his and found suddenly that it was no longer difficult. 'Well, we can't just stand here saying "well" at each other. Come on in and sit down. We've got a long time ahead of us – O Steve, isn't it wonderful! Hey. Didn't you bring a bag?'

'Why, you see,' he said, and stopped. He slung his cap over on to the table among the bottles and glasses. 'I left the bag at the station. I'm afraid I've got sort of rotten news, darling.'

She kept her hands from flying to her breast.

'You – you're going overseas right away?' she said.

'O Lord, no,' he said. 'Oh, no, no, no. I said this was rotten news. No. They've changed the orders, baby. They've taken back all leaves. We're to go right on to the new field. I've got to get a train at six-ten.'

She sat down on the sofa. She wanted to cry; not silently with slow crystal tears, but with wide mouth and smeared face. She wanted to throw herself stomach-down on the floor, and kick and scream, and go limp if anyone tried to lift her.

'I think that's awful,' she said. 'I think that's just filthy.'

'I know,' he said. 'But there's nothing to do about it. This is the army, Mrs Jones.'

'Couldn't you have said something?' she said. 'Couldn't you have told them you've had only one leave in six months? Couldn't you have said all the chance your wife had to see you again was just this poor little twenty-four hours? Couldn't you have explained what it meant to her? Couldn't you?'

'Come on, now, Mimi,' he said. 'There's a war on.'

'I'm sorry,' she said. 'I was sorry as soon as I'd said it. I was sorry while I was saying it. But – oh, it's so hard!'

'It's not easy for anybody,' he said. 'You don't know how the boys were looking forward to their leaves.'

'Oh, I don't give a damn about the boys!' she said.

'That's the spirit that'll win for our side,' he said. He sat down in the biggest chair, stretched his legs and crossed his ankles.

'You don't care about anything but those pilots,' she said.

'Look, Mimi,' he said. 'We haven't got time to do this. We haven't got time to get into a fight and say a lot of things we don't mean. Everything's all – all speeded up, now. There's no time left for this.'

'Oh, I know,' she said. 'O Steve, don't I know!'

She went over and sat on the arm of his chair and buried her face in his shoulder.

'This is more like it,' he said. 'I've kept thinking about this.' She nodded against his blouse.

'If you knew what it was to sit in a decent chair again,' he said.

She sat up. 'Oh,' she said. 'It's the chair. I'm so glad you like it.'

'They've got the worst chairs you ever saw, in the pilots' room,' he said. 'A lot of busted-down old rockers – honestly, rockers – that big-hearted patriots contributed, to get them out of the attic. If they haven't better furniture at the new field, I'm going to do something about it, even if I have to buy the stuff myself.'

'I certainly would, if I were you,' she said. 'I'd go without food and clothing and laundry, so the boys would be happy sitting down. I wouldn't even save out enough for air mail stamps, to write to my wife once in a while.'

She rose and moved about the room.

'Mimi, what's the matter with you?' he said. 'Are you – are you jealous of the pilots?'

She counted as far as eight, to herself. Then she turned and smiled at him.

'Why – I guess I am – ' she said. 'I guess that's just what I must be. Not only of the pilots. Of the whole air corps. Of the whole Army of the United States.'

'You're wonderful,' he said.

'You see,' she said with care, 'you have a whole new life – I have half an old one. Your life is so far away from mine, I don't see how they're ever going to come back together.'

'That's nonsense,' he said.

'No, please wait,' she said. 'I get strained and – and frightened, I guess, and I say things I could cut my throat for saying. But you know what I really feel about you. I'm so proud of you I can't find words for it. I know you're doing the most important thing in the world, maybe the only important thing in the world. Only – O Steve, I wish to heaven you didn't love doing it so much!'

'Listen,' he said.

'No,' she said. 'You mustn't interrupt a lady. It's unbecoming an officer, like carrying packages in the street. I'm just trying to tell you a little about how I feel. I can't get used to being so completely left out. You don't wonder what I do, you don't want to find out what's in my head – why, you never even ask me how I am!'

'I do so!' he said. 'I asked you how you were the minute I came in.'

'That was white of you,' she said.

'Oh, for Heaven's sake!' he said. 'I didn't have to ask you. I could see how you look. You look wonderful. I told you that.'

She smiled at him. 'Yes, you did, didn't you?' she said.

'And you sounded as if you meant it. Do you really like my dress?'

'Oh, yes,' he said. 'I always liked that dress on you.'

It was as if she turned to wood. 'This dress', she said, enunciating with insulting distinctness, 'is brand-new. I have never had it on before in my life. In case you are interested, I bought it especially for this occasion.'

'I'm sorry, honey,' he said. 'Oh, sure, now I see it's not the other one at all. I think it's great. I like you in black.'

'At moments like this', she said, 'I almost wish I were in it for another reason.'

'Stop it,' he said. 'Sit down and tell me about yourself. What have you been doing?'

'Oh, nothing,' she said.

'How's the office?' he said.

'Dull,' she said. 'Dull as mud.'

'Who have you seen?' he said.

'Oh, nobody,' she said.

'Well, what do you *do*?' he said.

'In the evenings?' she said. 'Oh, I sit here and knit and read detective stories that it turns out I've read before.'

'I think that's all wrong of you,' he said. 'I think it's asinine to sit here alone, moping. That doesn't do any good to anybody. Why don't you go out more?'

'I hate to go out with just women,' she said.

'Well, why do you have to?' he said. 'Ralph's in town, isn't he? And John and Bill and Gerald. Why don't you go out with them? You're silly not to.'

'It hadn't occurred to me', she said, 'that it was silly to keep faithful to one's husband.'

'Isn't that taking rather a jump?' he said. 'It's possible to go to dinner with a man and stay this side of adultery. And don't use words like "one's". You're awful when you're elegant.'

'I know,' she said. 'I never have any luck when I try. No. You're the one that's awful, Steve. You really are. I'm trying to show you a glimpse of my heart, to tell you how it feels when you're gone, how I don't want to be with anyone if I can't be with you. And all you say is, I'm not doing any good to anybody. That'll be nice to think of when you go. You don't know what it's like for me here alone. You just don't know.'

'Yes, I do,' he said. 'I know, Mimi.' He reached for a cigarette on the little table beside him, and the bright magazine by the cigarette-box caught his eye. 'Hey, is this this week's? I haven't seen it yet.' He glanced through the early pages.

'Go ahead and read if you want to,' she said. 'Don't let me disturb you.'

'I'm not reading,' he said. He put down the magazine. 'You see, I don't know what to say, when you start talking about showing me glimpses of your heart, and all that. I know. I know you must be having a rotten time. But aren't you feeling fairly sorry for yourself?'

'If *I'm* not,' she said, 'who would be?'

'What do you want anyone to be sorry for you for?' he said. 'You'd be all right if you'd stop sitting around alone. I'd like to think of you having a good time while I'm away.'

She went over to him and kissed him on the forehead.

'Lieutenant,' she said, 'you are a far nobler character than I am. Either that,' she said, 'or there is something else back of this.'

'Oh, shut up,' he said. He pulled her down to him and held her there. She seemed to melt against him, and stayed there, still.

Then she felt him take his left arm from around her and felt his head raised from its place against hers. She looked up at him. He was craning over her shoulder, endeavouring to see his wrist-watch.

'Oh, now, really!' she said. She put her hands against his chest and pushed herself vigorously away from him.

'It goes so quickly,' he said softly, with his eyes on his watch. 'We've – we've only a little while, darling.'

She melted again. 'O Steve,' she whispered. 'O dearest.'

'I do want to take a bath,' he said. 'Get up, will you, baby?'

She got right up. 'You're going to take a bath?' she said.

'Yes,' he said. 'You don't mind, do you?'

'Oh, not in the least,' she said. 'I'm sure you'll enjoy it. It's one of the pleasantest ways of killing time, I always think.'

'You know how you feel after a long ride on a train,' he said.

'Oh, surely,' she said.

He rose and went into the bedroom. 'I'll hurry up,' he called back to her.

'Why?' she said.

Then she had a moment to consider herself. She went into the bedroom after him, sweet with renewed resolve. He had hung his blouse and necktie neatly over a chair and he was unbuttoning his shirt. As she came in, he took it off. She looked at the beautiful brown triangle of his back. She would do anything for him, anything in the world.

'I – I'll go run your bath water,' she said. She went into the bathroom, turned on the faucets of the tub, and set the towels and mat ready. When she came back into the bedroom he was just entering it from the living-room, naked. In his hand he carried the bright magazine he had glanced at before. She stopped short.

'Oh,' she said. 'You're planning to read in the tub?'

'If you knew how I'd been looking forward to this!' he said. 'Boy, a hot bath in a tub! We haven't got anything but showers, and when you take a shower, there's a hundred boys waiting, yelling at you to hurry up and get out.'

'I suppose they can't bear being parted from you,' she said.

He smiled at her. 'See you in a couple of minutes,' he said, and went on into the bathroom and closed the door. She heard the slow slip and slide of water as he laid himself in the tub.

She stood just as she was. The room was lively with the perfume she had sprayed, too present, too insistent. Her eyes went to the bureau drawer where lay, wrapped in soft fragrance, the night-gown with the little bouquets and the Romney neck. She went over to the bathroom door, drew back her right foot, and kicked the base of the door so savagely that the whole frame shook.

'What, dear?' he called. 'Want something?'

'Oh, nothing,' she said. 'Nothing whatever. I've got everything any woman could possibly want, haven't I?'

'What?' he called. 'I can't hear you, honey.'

'Nothing,' she screamed.

She went into the living-room. She stood, breathing heavily, her finger-nails scarring her palms, as she looked at the fuchsia blossoms, with their dirty parchment-coloured cups, their vulgar magenta bells.

Her breath was quiet and her hands relaxed when he came into the living-room again. He had on his trousers and shirt, and his necktie was admirably knotted. He carried his belt. She turned to him. There were things she had meant to say, but she could do nothing but smile at him, when she saw him. Her heart turned liquid in her breast.

His brow was puckered. 'Look, darling,' he said. 'Have you got any brass polish?'

'Why, no,' she said. 'We haven't even got any brass.'

'Well, have you any nail polish – the colourless kind? A lot of the boys use that.'

'I'm sure it must look adorable on them,' she said. 'No. I haven't anything but rose-coloured polish. Would that be of any use to you, Heaven forbid?'

'No,' he said, and he seemed worried. 'Red wouldn't be any good at all. Hell, I don't suppose you've got a Blitz Cloth, have you? Or a Shine-O?'

'If I had the faintest idea what you were talking about,' she said, 'I might be better company for you.'

He held the belt out toward her. 'I want to shine my buckle,' he said.

'Oh . . . my . . . dear . . . sweet . . . gentle . . . Lord,' she said. 'We've got about ten minutes left, and you want to shine your belt buckle.'

'I don't like to report to a new CO with a dull belt buckle,' he said.

'It was bright enough for you to report to your wife in, wasn't it?' she said.

'Oh, stop that,' he said. 'You just won't understand, that's all.'

'It isn't that I won't understand,' she said. 'It's that I can't remember. I haven't been with a Boy Scout for so long.'

He looked at her. 'You're being great, aren't you?' he said. He looked around the room. 'There must be a cloth around somewhere – oh, this will do.' He caught up a pretty little cocktail napkin from the table of untouched bottles and glasses, sat down with his belt laid over his knees, and rubbed at the buckle.

She watched him for a moment, then rushed over to him and grasped his arm.

'Please,' she said. 'Please, I didn't mean it, Steve.'

'Please let me do this, will you?' he said. He wrenched his arm from her hand and went on with his polishing.

'You tell me I won't understand!' she cried. 'You won't understand anything about anybody else. Except those crazy pilots.'

'They're all right!' he said. 'They're fine kids. They're going to make great fighters.' He went on rubbing at his buckle.

'Oh, I know it!' she said. 'You know I know it. I don't mean it when I say things against them. How would I dare to mean it? They're risking their lives and their sight and their sanity, they're giving everything for — '

'Don't do that kind of talk, will you?' he said. He rubbed the buckle.

'I'm not doing any kind of talk!' she said. 'I'm trying to tell you something. Just because you've got on that pretty suit, you think you should never hear anything serious, never anything sad or wretched or disagreeable. You make me sick, that's what you do! I know, I know – I'm not trying to take anything away from you, I realise what you're doing, I told you what I think of it. Don't, for Heaven's sake, think I'm mean enough to grudge you any happiness and excitement you can get out of it. I know it's hard for you. But it's never lonely, that's all I mean. You have companionships no – no wife can ever give you. I suppose it's the sense of hurry, maybe, the consciousness of living on borrowed time, the – the knowledge of what you're all going into together that makes the comradeship of men in war so firm, so fast. But won't you please try to understand how I feel? Won't you understand that it comes out of bewilderment and disruption and – and being frightened, I guess? Won't you understand what makes me do what I do, when I hate myself while I'm doing it? Won't you please understand? Darling, won't you please?'

He laid down the little napkin. 'I can't go through this kind of thing, Mimi,' he said. 'Neither can you.' He looked at his watch. 'Hey, it's time for me to go.'

She stood tall and stiff. 'I'm sure it is,' she said.

'I'd better put on my blouse,' he said.

'You might as well,' she said.

He rose, wove his belt through the loops of his trousers, and went into the bedroom. She went over to the window and stood looking out, as if casually remarking the weather.

She heard him come back into the room, but she did not turn around. She heard his steps stop, knew he was standing there.

'Mimi,' he said.

She turned toward him, her shoulders back, her chin high, cool, regal. Then she saw his eyes. They were no longer bright and gay and confident. Their blue was misty and they looked troubled; they looked at her as if they pleaded with her.

'Look, Mimi,' he said, 'do you think I want to do this? Do you think I want to be away from you? Do you think that this is what I thought I'd be doing now? In the years – well, in the years when we ought to be together.'

He stopped. Then he spoke again, but with difficulty. 'I can't talk about it. I can't even think about it – because if I did I couldn't do my job. But just because I don't talk about it doesn't mean I want to be doing what I'm doing. I want to be with you, Mimi. That's where I belong. You know that, darling. Don't you?'

He held his arms open to her. She ran to them. This time, she did not slide her cheek along his lips.

When he had gone, she stood a moment by the fuchsia

plants, touching delicately, tenderly, the enchanting parchment-coloured cups, the exquisite magenta bells.

The telephone rang. She answered it, to hear a friend of hers enquiring about Steve, asking how he looked and how he was, urging that he come to the telephone and say hello to her.

'He's gone,' she said. 'All their leaves were cancelled. He wasn't here an hour.'

The friend cried sympathy. It was a shame, it was simply awful, it was absolutely terrible.

'No, don't say that,' she said. 'I know it wasn't very much time. But oh, it was lovely!'

Ballade of a Talked-off Ear

Daily I listen to wonder and woe,
Nightly I hearken to knave or to ace,
Telling me stories of lava and snow,
Delicate fables of ribbon and lace,
Tales of the quarry, the kill, the chase,
Longer than heaven and duller than hell –
Never you blame me, who cry my case:
'Poets alone should kiss and tell!'

Dumbly I hear what I never should know,
Gently I counsel of pride and of grace;
Into minutiae gaily they go,
Telling the name and the time and the place.
Cede them your silence and grant them space –
Who tenders an inch shall be raped of an ell!
Sympathy's ever the boaster's brace;
Poets alone should kiss and tell.

Why am I tithed what I never did owe?
Choked with vicarious saffron and mace?
Weary my lids, and my fingers are slow –
Gentlemen, damn you, you've halted my pace.
Only the lads of the cursèd race,
Only the knights of the desolate spell,
May point me the lines the blood-drops trace –
Poets alone should kiss and tell.

L'envoi

Prince or commoner, tenor or bass,
Painter or plumber or never-do-well,
Do me a favour and shut your face –
Poets alone should kiss and tell.

Prologue to a Saga

Maidens, gather not the yew,
  Leave the glossy myrtle sleeping;
Any lad was born untrue,
  Never a one is fit your weeping.

Pretty dears, your tumult cease;
  Love's a fardel, burthening double.
Clear your hearts, and have your peace –
  Gangway, girls: I'll show you trouble.

The Last Question

New love, new love, where are you to lead me?
  All along a narrow way that marks a crooked line.
How are you to slake me, and how are you to feed me?
  With bitter yellow berries, and a sharp new wine.

New love, new love, shall I be forsaken?
  One shall go a-wandering, and one of us must sigh.
Sweet it is to slumber, but how shall we awaken –
  Whose will be the broken heart, when dawn comes by?

COUSIN LARRY

The young woman in the crêpe de Chine dress printed all over with little pagodas set amid giant cornflowers flung one knee atop the other and surveyed, with an enviable contentment, the tip of her scrolled green sandal. Then, in a like happy calm, she inspected her finger-nails of so thick and glistening a red that it seemed as if she but recently had completed tearing an ox apart with her naked hands. Then she dropped her chin abruptly to her chest and busied herself among the man-made curls, sharp and dry as shavings, along the back of her neck; and again she appeared to be wrapped in cosy satisfaction. Then she lighted a fresh cigarette and seemed to find it, like all about her, good. Then she went right on with all she had been saying before.

'No, but really,' she said. 'Honestly. I get so darn sick of all this talk about Lila – "Oh, poor Lila" this, and "Oh, the poor thing" that. If they want to be sorry for her – well, it's a free country, I suppose, but all I can say is I think they're crazy. I think they're absolutely cock-eyed wild. If they want to be sorry for anybody, go be sorry for Cousin Larry, why don't they? Then they'd be making some sense for a change. Listen, nobody has to be sorry for Lila. She has a marvellous time; she never does one solitary thing she doesn't want to do. She has the best time of anybody I know. And anyway, it's all her own fault, anyway. It's just the way she is; it's her rotten, vile disposition. Well, you can't be expected to feel sorry for anybody when it's their own fault, can you? Does that make any sense? Now I ask you!

'Listen. I know Lila. I've known her for years. I've seen her practically day in, day out. Well, you know how often I've visited them, down in the country. You know how well you know a person after you've visited them; well, that's the way I know Lila. And I like her. Honestly I do. I like Lila all right when she's decent. It's only when she starts feeling sorry for herself and begins whining and asking questions and spoiling everybody's fun that she makes me throw up. A lot of the time she's perfectly all right. Only she's selfish, that's all. She's just a rotten, selfish woman. And then the way people talk about Larry for staying in town and going around places without her! Listen to me, she stays home because she wants to. She'd *rather* go to bed early. I've seen her do it night after night, when I've been down there visiting. I know her like a book. Catch *that* one doing anything she doesn't feel like doing!

'Honestly. It just makes me boil to hear anyone say anything against Larry. Just let them try criticising him to me, that's all. Why, that man's a living saint, that's what he is. How on earth he's got anything at all left, after ten years with that woman, I *don't* see. She can't let him alone a second; always wants to be in on everything, always wants to know what's the joke and what's he laughing about, and oh, tell her, tell her, so she can laugh too. And she's one of those damn serious old fools that can't see anything funny, and can't kid or anything, and then she tries to get cute and play, too, and – well, you just can't *look*, that's all. And poor Larry, who couldn't be funnier or have more of a sense of humour and all. I should think she'd have driven him cock-eyed wild, years ago.

'And then when she sees the poor soul having a little bit of fun with anybody for a few minutes, she gets – well, she doesn't get jealous, she's too self-centred ever to have a jealous moment – she's so rotten suspicious, she's got such a vile, dirty mind, she just gets mean. And to me, of all people. Now I ask you! Me, that's known Larry practically all my life, practically. Why, I've called him Cousin Larry for years – that shows you how I've always felt about him. And the very first time I went down there to stay with them, she started in about why did I call him Cousin Larry, and I said, oh, I'd known him so well, I felt sort of related, and then she got kittenish, the old fool, and said, well, I'd have to take her into the family, too, and I said yes, that would be great, or something. And I *did* try to call her Aunt Lila, but I just simply couldn't seem to *feel* that way. And it didn't seem to make her any happier, anyway. Well, she's just one of those kind; she's never happy unless she's miserable. She *enjoys* being miserable. That's why she does it. Catch her doing anything she doesn't want to do!

'Honestly. Poor Cousin Larry. Imagine that dirty old thing

trying to work up something, because I call him Cousin Larry. Well, I certainly didn't let her stop me; I guess my friendship with Larry is worth a little more than *that*. And he calls me Little Sweetheart, too, just the way he always did. He's always called me his little sweetheart. Wouldn't you think she could see, if there was anything in it, he wouldn't call me that right in front of her face all the time?

'Really. It isn't that she means anything in my young life, it's just that I feel so terribly sorry for Larry. I wouldn't set foot in the house again if it wasn't for him. But he says – of course, he's never said one single word against her, he's the kind would always be just like a clam about any woman that happened to be his wife – he says nobody has any idea of what it's like to be there alone with Lila. So that's why I went down in the first place. And I saw what he meant. Why, the first night I was in the house, she went up to bed at ten o'clock. Cousin Larry and I were playing some old phonograph records – well, we had to do *something*, she wouldn't laugh or kid or do anything we were doing, just sat there like an old stick – and it just happened I happened to find a lot of old songs Larry and I used to sing and go dancing to, and everything. Well, you know how it is when you know a man awfully well, you always have things that remind you of things, and we were laughing and playing these records and sort of saying, "Do you remember the time?" and "What does that remind you of?" and all, the way everybody does; and the first thing you know, Lila got up and said she was sure we wouldn't mind if she went to bed – she felt so awfully tired. And Larry told me then, that's what she always does when anybody around is having a good time. If there's a guest in the house when she feels so awfully tired, that's just too bad, that's all. A little thing like that doesn't put *that* one out. When she wants to go to bed, she *goes*.

'So that's why I've gone down there so much. You don't know what a real godsend it is for Larry to have someone he can sit up with, after dear Lila goes to bed at ten o'clock. And then I'm somebody the poor soul can play golf with in the daytime, too; Lila can't play – oh, she's got something wrong with her insides, *wouldn't* she have? I wouldn't go near the place if it wasn't such a help to Larry. You know how crazy he is about having a good time. And Lila's *old* – she's an *owe-wuld* woman! Honestly. Larry – well, of course it doesn't make any difference how old a man is, anyway – years, I mean; it's the way he feels that counts. And Larry's just like a kid. I keep telling Lila, trying to clean up her nasty, evil mind, that Cousin Larry and I are nothing but a couple of crazy kids together. Now I ask you, wouldn't you think she'd have sense enough to see she's all through and the only thing for her to do is to sit back and let people have a good time that *can*? *She* had a good time; going to bed early, that's what she likes. Nobody interferes with her – wouldn't you think she'd mind her own business and stop asking questions and wanting to know what everything's about?

'Well, now look. Once I was down there, and I happened to be wearing orchids. And so Lila said oh, weren't they lovely and all, and who sent them to me. Honestly. She *deliberately* asked me who sent them to me. So I thought, well, it will just do you good, and I told her Cousin Larry did. I told her it was a sort of a little anniversary of ours – you know how it is, when you know a man a long time, you always have sort of little anniversaries, like the first time he ever took you to lunch, or the first time he sent you flowers or something. So anyway, this was one of those, and I told Lila what a wonderful friend Cousin Larry was to me, and how he always remembered things like that, and how much fun it was for him to do them, he seemed to get such pleasure out of doing sweet things. Now I ask you. Wouldn't you think anybody in the *world* would see how innocent it was if you told them that? And do you know what she said? Honestly. She said, "I like orchids too." So I just thought, well, maybe if you were fifteen years younger you might get some man to send you some, baby, but I didn't say a thing. I just said, "Oh, wear these, Lila, won't you?" Just like that; and Lord knows, I didn't *have* to say it, did I? But oh, no, she wouldn't. No, she thought she'd just go and lie down a while, if I didn't mind. She was feeling so awfully tired.

'And then – oh, my dear, I nearly forgot to tell you. You'll simply die over this, you'll absolutely collapse. Well, the last time I was there, Cousin Larry had sent me some little chiffon drawers; they couldn't have been cuter. You know, it was just a joke, these little pink chiffon things with "*Mais l'amour viendra*" embroidered on them in black. It means "Love will come." You know. He saw them in some window and he just sent them to me, just for this joke. He's always doing things like – hey, for goodness' sake, don't tell anyone, will you? Because, Lord knows if it *meant* anything, I wouldn't be telling you, you *know* that, but you know how people are. And there's been enough talk, just because I go out with him sometimes, to keep the poor soul company while Lila's in bed.

'Well, so anyway, he sent me these things, and so when I came down to dinner – there were just the three of us; that's another thing she does, she doesn't have anybody in unless he absolutely insists – I said to Larry, "I've got them on, Cousin Larry." So of course Lila had to hear and she said, "What have you got on?" and she kept asking and asking, and naturally I wasn't going to tell *her*, and it just struck me so funny I nearly died trying not to laugh and every time I caught Larry's eye we'd both bust right out. And Lila kept saying oh, what was the joke, and oh, tell her, tell her. And so finally, when she saw we wouldn't tell, she had to go to bed, no matter how it made *us* feel. My God, can't people have jokes? This is a free country, isn't it?

'Honestly. And she's getting worse and worse all the time. I'm simply *sick* about Larry. I can't see what he's ever going to do. You know a woman like that wouldn't give a man a divorce in a million years, even if he was the one that had the money. Larry never says a word, but I bet there are times when he just wishes she'd *die*. And everybody saying, "Oh, poor Lila", "Oh, poor, dear Lila, isn't it a shame?" That's because she gets them off in corners, and starts sobbing about not having any children. Oh, how she wishes she had a baby. Oh, if she and Larry only had a baby, blah, blah, blah, blah, blah. And then the eyes filling with tears – you know, you've seen her do it. Eyes filling with tears! A lot she's got to cry about, always doing what she wants all the time. I bet that's just a line, about not having a baby. That's just to get sympathy. She's just so rotten selfish she wouldn't have ever given up her own convenience to have one, that's what's the matter with her. She might have had to stay up after ten o'clock.

'Poor Lila! Honestly, I could lose my lunch. Why don't they say poor Larry, for a change? He's the one to feel sorry for. Well. All *I* know is, I'll always do anything I can for Cousin Larry. That's all *I* know.'

The young woman in the printed crêpe de Chine dress removed her dead cigarette from its pasteboard holder and seemed, as she did so, to find increased enjoyment in the familiar sight of her rich-hued finger-nails. Then she took from her lap a case of gold or some substance near it, and in a minute mirror scanned her face as carefully as if it were verse. She knit her brows, she drew her upper eyelids nearly to those below them, she turned her head as one expressing regretful negation, she moved her mouth laterally in the manner of a semi-tropical fish; and when all this was done, she seemed even cooler in confidence of well-being. Then she lighted a fresh cigarette and appeared to find that, too, impeccable. Then she went right on over all she had been saying before.

BIG BLONDE

Hazel Morse was a large, fair woman of the type that incites some men when they use the word 'blonde' to click their tongues and wag their heads roguishly. She prided herself upon her small feet and suffered for her vanity, boxing them in snub-toed, high-heeled slippers of the shortest bearable size. The curious things about her were her hands, strange terminations to the flabby white arms splattered with pale tan spots – long, quivering hands with deep and convex nails. She should not have disfigured them with little jewels.

She was not a woman given to recollections. At her middle thirties, her old days were a blurred and flickering sequence, an imperfect film, dealing with the actions of strangers.

In her twenties, after the deferred death of a hazy widowed mother, she had been employed as a model in a wholesale dress establishment – it was still the day of the big woman, and she was then prettily coloured and erect and high-breasted. Her job was not onerous, and she met numbers of men and spent numbers of evenings with them, laughing at their jokes and telling them she loved their neckties. Men liked her, and she took it for granted that the liking of many men was a desirable thing. Popularity seemed to her to be worth all the work that had to be put into its achievement. Men liked you because you were fun, and when they liked you they took you out, and there you were. So, and successfully, she was fun. She was a good sport. Men liked a good sport.

No other form of diversion, simpler or more complicated, drew her attention. She never pondered if she might not be better occupied doing something else. Her ideas, or, better, her acceptances, ran right along with those of the other substantially built blondes in whom she found her friends.

When she had been working in the dress establishment some years she met Herbie Morse. He was thin, quick, attractive, with shifting lines about his shiny, brown eyes and a habit of fiercely biting at the skin around his finger-nails. He drank largely; she found that entertaining. Her habitual greeting to him was an allusion to his state of the previous night.

'Oh, what a peach you had,' she used to say, through her easy laugh. 'I thought I'd die, the way you kept asking the waiter to dance with you.'

She liked him immediately upon their meeting. She was enormously amused at his fast, slurred sentences, his interpolations of apt phrases from vaudeville acts and comic strips; she thrilled at the feel of his lean arm tucked firm beneath the sleeve of her coat; she wanted to touch the wet, flat surface of his hair. He was as promptly drawn to her. They were married six weeks after they had met.

She was delighted at the idea of being a bride; coquetted with it, played upon it. Other offers of marriage she had had, and not a few of them, but it happened that they were all from stout, serious men who had visited the dress establishment as buyers; men from Des Moines and Houston and Chicago and, in her phrase, even funnier places. There was always something immensely comic to her in the thought of living elsewhere than New York. She could not regard as serious proposals that she share a western residence.

She wanted to be married. She was nearing thirty now, and she did not take the years well. She spread and softened, and her darkening hair turned her to inexpert dabblings with peroxide. There were times when she had little flashes of fear about her job. And she had had a couple of thousand evenings of being a good sport among her male acquaintances. She had come to be more conscientious than spontaneous about it.

Herbie earned enough, and they took a little apartment far uptown. There was a mission-furnished dining-room with a hanging central light globed in liver-coloured glass; in the living-room were an 'over-stuffed suite', a Boston fern, and a reproduction of the Henner 'Magdalene' with the red hair and the blue draperies; the bedroom was in grey enamel and old rose, with Herbie's photograph on Hazel's dressing-table and Hazel's likeness on Herbie's chest of drawers.

She cooked – and she was a good cook – and marketed and chatted with the delivery boys and the coloured laundress.

She loved the flat, she loved her life, she loved Herbie. In the first months of their marriage, she gave him all the passion she was ever to know.

She had not realised how tired she was. It was a delight, a new game, a holiday, to give up being a good sport. If her head ached or her arches throbbed, she complained piteously, babyishly. If her mood was quiet, she did not talk. If tears came to her eyes, she let them fall.

She fell readily into the habit of tears during the first year of her marriage. Even in her good sport days, she had been known to weep lavishly and disinterestedly on occasion. Her behaviour at the theatre was a standing joke. She could weep at anything in a play – tiny garments, love both unrequited and mutual, seduction, purity, faithful servitors, wedlock, the triangle.

'There goes Haze,' her friends would say, watching her. 'She's off again.'

Wedded and relaxed, she poured her tears freely. To her who had laughed so much, crying was delicious. All sorrows became her sorrows; she was Tenderness. She would cry long and softly over newspaper accounts of kidnapped babies, deserted wives, unemployed men, strayed cats, heroic dogs. Even when the paper was no longer before her, her mind revolved upon these things and the drops slipped rhythmically over her plump cheeks.

'Honestly,' she would say to Herbie, 'all the sadness there is in the world when you stop to think about it!'

'Yeah,' Herbie would say.

She missed nobody. The old crowd, the people who had brought her and Herbie together, dropped from their lives, lingeringly at first. When she thought of this at all, it was only to consider it fitting. This was marriage. This was peace.

But the thing was that Herbie was not amused.

For a time, he had enjoyed being alone with her. He found the voluntary isolation novel and sweet. Then it palled with a ferocious suddenness. It was as if one night, sitting with her in the steam-heated living-room, he would ask no more; and the next night he was through and done with the whole thing.

He became annoyed by her misty melancholies. At first, when he came home to find her softly tired and moody, he kissed her neck and patted her shoulder and begged her to tell her Herbie what was wrong. She loved that. But time slid by, and he found that there was never anything really, personally, the matter.

'Ah, for God's sake,' he would say. 'Crabbing again. All right, sit here and crab your head off. I'm going out.'

And he would slam out of the flat and come back late and drunk.

She was completely bewildered by what happened to their marriage. First they were lovers; and then, it seemed without transition, they were enemies. She never understood it.

There were longer and longer intervals between his leaving his office and his arrival at the apartment. She went through agonies of picturing him run over and bleeding, dead and covered with a sheet. Then she lost her fears for his safety and grew sullen and wounded. When a person wanted to be with a person, he came as soon as possible. She desperately wanted him to want to be with her; her own hours only marked the time till he would come. It was often nearly nine o'clock before he came home to dinner. Always he had had many drinks, and their effect would die in him, leaving him loud and querulous and bristling for affronts.

He was too nervous, he said, to sit and do nothing for an evening. He boasted, probably not in all truth, that he had never read a book in his life.

'What am I expected to do – sit around this dump on my tail all night?' he would ask, rhetorically. And again he would slam out.

She did not know what to do. She could not manage him. She could not meet him.

She fought him furiously. A terrific domesticity had come upon her, and she would bite and scratch to guard it. She wanted what she called 'a nice home'. She wanted a sober, tender husband, prompt at dinner, punctual at work. She wanted sweet, comforting evenings. The idea of intimacy with other men was terrible to her; the thought that Herbie might be seeking entertainment in other women set her frantic.

It seemed to her that almost everything she read – novels from the drugstore lending library, magazine stories, women's pages in the papers – dealt with wives who lost their husbands' love. She could bear those, at that, better than accounts of neat, companionable marriage and living happily ever after.

She was frightened. Several times when Herbie came home in the evening, he found her determinedly dressed – she had had to alter those of her clothes that were not new, to make them fasten – and rouged.

'Let's go wild tonight, what do you say?' she would hail him. 'A person's got lots of time to hang around and do nothing when they're dead.'

So they would go out, to chop houses and the less expensive cabarets. But it turned out badly. She could no longer find amusement in watching Herbie drink. She could not laugh at his whimsicalities, she was so tensely counting his indulgences. And she was unable to keep back her remonstrances – 'Ah, come on, Herb, you've had enough, haven't you? You'll feel something terrible in the morning.'

He would be immediately enraged. All right, crab; crab, crab, crab, crab, that was all she ever did. What a lousy sport *she* was! There would be scenes, and one or the other of them would rise and stalk out in fury.

She could not recall the definite day that she started drinking, herself. There was nothing separate about her days. Like drops upon a window-pane, they ran together and trickled away. She had been married six months; then a year; then three years.

She had never needed to drink, formerly. She could sit for most of a night at a table where the others were imbibing earnestly and never droop in looks or spirits, nor be bored by the doings of those about her. If she took a cocktail, it was so unusual as to cause twenty minutes or so of jocular comment. But now anguish was in her. Frequently, after a quarrel, Herbie would stay out for the night, and she could not learn from him where the time had been spent. Her heart felt tight and sore in her breast, and her mind turned like an electric fan.

She hated the taste of liquor. Gin, plain or in mixtures, made her promptly sick. After experiment, she found that Scotch whisky was best for her. She took it without water, because that was the quickest way to its effect.

Herbie pressed it on her. He was glad to see her drink. They both felt it might restore her high spirits, and their good times together might again be possible.

''Atta girl,' he would approve her. 'Let's see you get boiled, baby.'

But it brought them no nearer. When she drank with him, there would be a little while of gaiety and then, strangely without beginning, they would be in a wild quarrel. They would wake in the morning not sure what it had all been about, foggy as to what had been said and done, but each deeply injured and bitterly resentful. There would be days of vengeful silence.

There had been a time when they had made up their quarrels, usually in bed. There would be kisses and little names and assurances of fresh starts . . . 'Oh, it's going to be great now, Herb. We'll have swell times. I was a crab. I guess I must have been tired. But everything's going to be swell. You'll see.'

Now there were no gentle reconciliations. They resumed friendly relations only in the brief magnanimity caused by liquor, before more liquor drew them into new battles. The scenes became more violent. There were shouted invectives and pushes, and sometimes sharp slaps. Once she had a black eye. Herbie was horrified next day at sight of it. He did not go to work; he followed her about, suggesting remedies and heaping dark blame on himself. But after they had had a few drinks – 'to pull themselves together' – she made so many wistful references to her bruise that he shouted at her and rushed out and was gone for two days.

Each time he left the place in a rage, he threatened never to come back. She did not believe him, nor did she consider separation. Somewhere in her head or her heart was the lazy, nebulous hope that things would change and she and Herbie settle suddenly into soothing married life. Here were her home, her furniture, her husband, her station. She summoned no alternatives.

She could no longer bustle and potter. She had no more vicarious tears; the hot drops she shed were for herself. She walked ceaselessly about the rooms, her thoughts running mechanically round and round Herbie. In those days began the hatred of being alone that she was never to overcome. You could be by yourself when things were all right, but when you were blue you got the howling horrors.

She commenced drinking alone, little, short drinks all through the day. It was only with Herbie that alcohol made her nervous and quick in offence. Alone, it blurred sharp things for her. She lived in a haze of it. Her life took on a dream-like quality. Nothing was astonishing.

A Mrs Martin moved into the flat across the hall. She was a great blonde woman of forty, a promise in looks of what Mrs Morse was to be. They made acquaintance, quickly became inseparable. Mrs Morse spent her days in the opposite apartment. They drank together, to brace themselves after the drinks of the nights before.

She never confided her troubles about Herbie to Mrs Martin. The subject was too bewildering to her to find comfort in talk. She let it be assumed that her husband's business kept him much away. It was not regarded as important; husbands, as such, played but shadowy parts in Mrs Martin's circle.

Mrs Martin had no visible spouse; you were left to decide for yourself whether he was or was not dead. She had an admirer, Joe, who came to see her almost nightly. Often he brought several friends with him – 'The Boys', they were called. The Boys were big, red, good-humoured men, perhaps forty-five, perhaps fifty. Mrs Morse was glad of invitations to join the parties – Herbie was scarcely ever at home at night now. If he did come home, she did not visit Mrs Martin. An evening alone with Herbie meant inevitably a quarrel, yet she would stay with him. There was always her thin and wordless idea that, maybe, this night, things would begin to be all right.

The Boys brought plenty of liquor along with them whenever they came to Mrs Martin's. Drinking with them, Mrs Morse became lively and good-natured and audacious. She was quickly popular. When she had drunk enough to cloud her most recent battle with Herbie, she was excited by their approbation. Crab, was she? Rotten sport, was she? Well, there were some that thought different.

Ed was one of The Boys. He lived in Utica – had 'his own business' there, was the awed report – but he came to New York almost every week. He was married. He showed Mrs Morse the then current photographs of Junior and Sister, and she praised them abundantly and sincerely. Soon it was accepted by the others that Ed was her particular friend.

He staked her when they all played poker; sat next her and occasionally rubbed his knee against hers during the game. She was rather lucky. Frequently she went home with a twenty-dollar bill or a ten-dollar bill or a handful of crumpled dollars. She was glad of them. Herbie was getting, in her words, something awful about money. To ask him for it brought an instant row.

'What the hell do you do with it?' he would say. 'Shoot it all on Scotch?'

'I try to run this house half-way decent,' she would retort. 'Never thought of that, did you? Oh, no, his lordship couldn't be bothered with that.'

Again, she could not find a definite day, to fix the beginning of Ed's proprietorship. It became his custom to kiss her on the mouth when he came in, as well as for farewell, and he gave her little quick kisses of approval all through the evening. She liked this rather more than she disliked it. She never thought of his kisses when she was not with him.

He would run his hand lingeringly over her back and shoulders.

'Some dizzy blonde, eh?' he would say. 'Some doll.'

One afternoon she came home from Mrs Martin's to find Herbie in the bedroom. He had been away for several nights, evidently on a prolonged drinking bout. His face was grey, his hands jerked as if they were on wires. On the bed were two old suitcases, packed high. Only her photograph remained on his bureau, and the wide doors of his closet disclosed nothing but coat-hangers.

'I'm blowing,' he said. 'I'm through with the whole works. I got a job in Detroit.'

She sat down on the edge of the bed. She had drunk much the night before, and the four Scotches she had had with Mrs Martin had only increased her fogginess.

'Good job?' she said.

'Oh, yeah,' he said. 'Looks all right.'

He closed a suitcase with difficulty, swearing at it in whispers.

'There's some dough in the bank,' he said. 'The bank book's in your top drawer. You can have the furniture and stuff.'

He looked at her, and his forehead twitched.

'God damn it, I'm through, I'm telling you,' he cried. 'I'm through.'

'All right, all right,' she said. 'I heard you, didn't I?'

She saw him as if he were at one end of a cannon and she at the other. Her head was beginning to ache bumpingly, and her voice had a dreary, tiresome tone. She could not have raised it.

'Like a drink before you go?' she asked.

Again he looked at her, and a corner of his mouth jerked up.

'Cock-eyed again for a change, aren't you?' he said. 'That's nice. Sure, get a couple of shots, will you?'

She went to the pantry, mixed him a stiff highball, poured herself a couple of inches of whisky and drank it. Then she gave herself another portion and brought the glasses into the bedroom. He had strapped both suitcases and had put on his hat and overcoat.

He took his highball.

'Well,' he said, and he gave a sudden, uncertain laugh. 'Here's mud in your eye.'

'Mud in your eye,' she said.

They drank. He put down his glass and took up the heavy suitcases.

'Got to get a train around six,' he said.

She followed him down the hall. There was a song, a song that Mrs Martin played doggedly on the phonograph, running loudly through her mind. She had never liked the thing.

'Night and daytime,
Always playtime.
Ain't we got fun?'

At the door he put down the bags and faced her.

'Well,' he said. 'Well, take care of yourself. You'll be all right, will you?'

'Oh, sure,' she said.

He opened the door, then came back to her, holding out his hand.

' 'Bye, Haze,' he said. 'Good luck to you.'

She took his hand and shook it.

'Pardon my wet glove,' she said.

When the door had closed behind him, she went back to the pantry.

She was flushed and lively when she went in to Mrs Martin's that evening. The Boys were there, Ed among them. He was glad to be in town, frisky and loud and full of jokes. But she spoke quietly to him for a minute.

'Herbie blew today,' she said. 'Going to live out west.'

'That so?' he said. He looked at her and played with the fountain pen clipped to his waistcoat pocket.

'Think he's gone for good, do you?' he asked.

'Yeah,' she said. 'I know he is. I know. Yeah.'

'You going to live on across the hall just the same?' he said. 'Know what you're going to do?'

'Gee, I don't know,' she said. 'I don't give much of a damn.'

'Oh, come on, that's no way to talk,' he told her. 'What you need – you need a little snifter. How about it?'

'Yeah,' she said. 'Just straight.'

She won forty-three dollars at poker. When the game

broke up, Ed took her back to her apartment.

'Got a little kiss for me?' he asked.

He wrapped her in his big arms and kissed her violently. She was entirely passive. He held her away and looked at her.

'Little tight, honey?' he asked, anxiously. 'Not going to be sick, are you?'

'Me?' she said. 'I'm swell.'

II

When Ed left in the morning, he took her photograph with him. He said he wanted her picture to look at, up in Utica. 'You can have that one on the bureau,' she said.

She put Herbie's picture in a drawer, out of her sight. When she could look at it, she meant to tear it up. She was fairly successful in keeping her mind from racing around him. Whisky slowed it for her. She was almost peaceful, in her mist.

She accepted her relationship with Ed without question or enthusiasm. When he was away, she seldom thought definitely of him. He was good to her; he gave her frequent presents and a regular allowance. She was even able to save. She did not plan ahead of any day, but her wants were few, and you might as well put money in the bank as have it lying around.

When the lease of her apartment neared its end, it was Ed who suggested moving. His friendship with Mrs Martin and Joe had become strained over a dispute at poker; a feud was impending.

'Let's get the hell out of here,' Ed said. 'What I want you to have is a place near the Grand Central. Make it easier for me.'

So she took a little flat in the Forties. A coloured maid came in every day to clean and to make coffee for her – she was 'through with that housekeeping stuff', she said, and Ed, twenty years married to a passionately domestic woman, admired this romantic uselessness and felt doubly a man of the world in abetting it.

The coffee was all she had until she went out to dinner, but alcohol kept her fat. Prohibition she regarded only as a basis for jokes. You could always get all you wanted. She was never noticeably drunk and seldom nearly sober. It required a larger daily allowance to keep her misty-minded. Too little, and she was achingly melancholy.

Ed brought her to Jimmy's. He was proud, with the pride of the transient who would be mistaken for a native, in his knowledge of small, recent restaurants occupying the lower floors of shabby brownstone houses; places where, upon mentioning the name of an *habitué* friend, might be obtained strange whisky and fresh gin in many of their ramifications. Jimmy's place was the favourite of his acquaintances.

There, through Ed, Mrs Morse met many men and women, formed quick friendships. The men often took her out when Ed was in Utica. He was proud of her popularity.

She fell into the habit of going to Jimmy's alone when she had no engagement. She was certain to meet some people she knew, and join them. It was a club for her friends, both men and women.

The women at Jimmy's looked remarkably alike, and this was curious, for, through feuds, removals, and opportunities of more profitable contacts, the personnel of the group changed constantly. Yet always the newcomers resembled those whom they replaced. They were all big women and stout, broad of shoulder and abundantly breasted, with faces thickly clothed in soft, high-coloured flesh. They laughed loud and often, showing opaque and lustreless teeth like squares of crockery. There was about them the health of the big, yet a slight, unwholesome suggestion of stubborn preservation. They might have been thirty-six or forty-five or anywhere between.

They composed their titles of their own first names with their husbands' surnames – Mrs Florence Miller, Mrs Vera Riley, Mrs Lilian Block. This gave at the same time the solidity of marriage and the glamour of freedom. Yet only one or two were actually divorced. Most of them never referred to their dimmed spouses; some, a shorter time separated, described them in terms of great biological interest. Several were mothers, each of an only child – a boy at school somewhere, or a girl being cared for by a grandmother. Often, well on toward morning, there would be displays of Kodak portraits and of tears.

They were comfortable women, cordial and friendly and irrepressibly matronly. Theirs was the quality of ease. Become fatalistic, especially about money matters, they were unworried. Whenever their funds dropped alarmingly, a new donor appeared; this had always happened. The aim of each was to have one man, permanently, to pay all her bills, in return for which she would have immediately given up other admirers and probably would have become exceedingly fond of him; for the affections of all of them were, by now, unexacting, tranquil, and easily arranged. This end, however, grew increasingly difficult yearly. Mrs Morse was regarded as fortunate.

Ed had a good year, increased her allowance and gave her a sealskin coat. But she had to be careful of her moods with him. He insisted upon gaiety. He would not listen to admissions of aches or weariness.

'Hey, listen,' he would say, 'I got worries of my own, and plenty. Nobody wants to hear other people's troubles, sweetie. What you got to do, you got to be a sport and forget it. See? Well, slip us a little smile, then. That's my girl.'

She never had enough interest to quarrel with him as she had with Herbie, but she wanted the privilege of occasional admitted sadness. It was strange. The other women she saw did not have to fight their moods. There was Mrs Florence Miller who got regular crying jags, and the men sought only to cheer and comfort her. The others spent whole evenings in grieved recitals of worries and ills; their escorts paid them deep sympathy. But she was instantly undesirable when she was low in spirits. Once, at Jimmy's, when she could not make herself lively, Ed had walked out and left her.

'Why the hell don't you stay home and not go spoiling everybody's evening?' he had roared.

Even her slightest acquaintances seemed irritated if she were not conspicuously light-hearted.

'What's the matter with you, anyway?' they would say. 'Be your age, why don't you? Have a little drink and snap out of it.'

When her relationship with Ed had continued nearly

three years, he moved to Florida to live. He hated leaving her; he gave her a large cheque and some shares of a sound stock, and his pale eyes were wet when he said goodbye. She did not miss him. He came to New York infrequently, perhaps two or three times a year, and hurried directly from the train to see her. She was always pleased to have him come and never sorry to see him go.

Charley, an acquaintance of Ed's that she had met at Jimmy's, had long admired her. He had always made opportunities of touching her and leaning close to talk to her. He asked repeatedly of all their friends if they had ever heard such a fine laugh as she had. After Ed left, Charley became the main figure in her life. She classified him and spoke of him as 'not so bad'. There was nearly a year of Charley; then she divided her time between him and Sydney, another frequenter of Jimmy's; then Charley slipped away altogether.

Sydney was a little, brightly dressed, clever Jew. She was perhaps nearest contentment with him. He amused her always; her laughter was not forced.

He admired her completely. Her softness and size delighted him. And he thought she was great, he often told her, because she kept gay and lively when she was drunk.

'Once I had a gal,' he said, 'used to try and throw herself out of the window every time she got a can on. Jee-*zuss*,' he added, feelingly.

Then Sydney married a rich and watchful bride, and then there was Billy. No – after Sydney came Fred, then Billy. In her haze, she never recalled how men entered her life and left it. There were no surprises. She had no thrill at their advent, nor woe at their departure. She seemed to be always able to attract men. There was never another as rich as Ed, but they were all generous to her, in their means.

Once she had news of Herbie. She met Mrs Martin dining at Jimmy's, and the old friendship was vigorously renewed. The still admiring Joe, while on a business trip, had seen Herbie. He had settled in Chicago, he looked fine, he was living with some woman – seemed to be crazy about her. Mrs Morse had been drinking vastly that day. She took the news with mild interest, as one hearing of the sex peccadilloes of somebody whose name is, after a moment's groping, familiar.

'Must be damn near seven years since I saw him,' she commented. 'Gee. Seven years.'

More and more, her days lost their individuality. She never knew dates, nor was sure of the day of the week.

'My God, was that a year ago!' she would exclaim, when an event was recalled in conversation.

She was tired so much of the time. Tired and blue. Almost everything could give her the blues. Those old horses she saw on Sixth Avenue – struggling and slipping along the car-tracks, or standing at the kerb, their heads dropped level with their worn knees. The tightly stored tears would squeeze from her eyes as she teetered past on her aching feet in the stubby, champagne-coloured slippers.

The thought of death came and stayed with her and lent her a sort of drowsy cheer. It would be nice, nice and restful, to be dead.

There was no settled, shocked moment when she first thought of killing herself; it seemed to her as if the idea had always been with her. She pounced upon all the accounts of suicides in the newspapers. There was an epidemic of self-killings – or maybe it was just that she searched for the stories of them so eagerly that she found many. To read of them roused reassurance in her; she felt a cosy solidarity with the big company of the voluntary dead.

She slept, aided by whisky, till deep into the afternoons, then lay abed, a bottle and glass at her hand, until it was time to dress and go out for dinner. She was beginning to feel toward alcohol a little puzzled distrust, as toward an old friend who has refused a simple favour. Whisky could still soothe her for most of the time, but there were sudden, inexplicable moments when the cloud fell treacherously away from her, and she was sawed by the sorrow and bewilderment and nuisance of all living. She played voluptuously with the thought of cool, sleepy retreat. She had never been troubled by religious belief and no vision of an afterlife intimidated her. She dreamed by day of never again putting on tight shoes, of never having to laugh and listen and admire, of never more being a good sport. Never.

But how would you do it? It made her sick to think of jumping from heights. She could not stand a gun. At the theatre, if one of the actors drew a revolver, she crammed her fingers into her ears and could not even look at the stage until after the shot had been fired. There was no gas in her flat. She looked long at the bright blue veins in her slim wrists – a cut with a razor blade, and there you'd be. But it would hurt, hurt like hell, and there would be blood to see. Poison – something tasteless and quick and painless – was the thing. But they wouldn't sell it to you in drugstores, because of the law.

She had few other thoughts.

There was a new man now – Art. He was short and fat and exacting and hard on her patience when he was drunk. But there had been only occasionals for some time before him, and she was glad of a little stability. Too, Art must be away for weeks at a stretch, selling silks, and that was restful. She was convincingly gay with him, though the effort shook her.

'The best sport in the world,' he would murmur, deep in her neck. 'The best sport in the world.'

One night, when he had taken her to Jimmy's, she went into the dressing-room with Mrs Florence Miller. There, while designing curly mouths on their faces with lip-rouge, they compared experiences of insomnia.

'Honestly,' Mrs Morse said, 'I wouldn't close an eye if I didn't go to bed full of Scotch. I lie there and toss and turn and toss and turn. Blue! Does a person get blue lying awake that way!'

'Say, listen, Hazel,' Mrs Miller said, impressively, 'I'm telling you I'd be awake for a year if I didn't take veronal. That stuff makes you sleep like a fool.'

'Isn't it poison, or something?' Mrs Morse asked.

'Oh, you take too much and you're out for the count,' said Mrs Miller. 'I just take five grains – they come in tablets. I'd be scared to fool around with it. But five grains, and you cork off pretty.'

'Can you get it anywhere?' Mrs Morse felt superbly machiavellian.

'Get all you want in Jersey,' said Mrs Miller. 'They won't give it to you here without you have a doctor's prescription. Finished? We'd better go back and see what the boys are doing.'

That night, Art left Mrs Morse at the door of her apartment; his mother was in town. Mrs Morse was still sober, and it happened that there was no whisky left in her cupboard. She lay in bed, looking up at the black ceiling.

She rose early, for her, and went to New Jersey. She had never taken the tube, and did not understand it. So she went to the Pennsylvania Station and bought a railroad ticket to Newark. She thought of nothing in particular on the trip out. She looked at the uninspired hats of the women about her and gazed through the smeared window at the flat, gritty scene.

In Newark, in the first drugstore she came to, she asked for a tin of talcum powder, a nailbrush, and a box of veronal tablets. The powder and the brush were to make the hypnotic seem also a casual need. The clerk was entirely unconcerned. 'We only keep them in bottles,' he said, and wrapped up for her a little glass vial containing ten white tablets, stacked one on another.

She went to another drugstore and bought a face-cloth, an orange-wood stick, and a bottle of veronal tablets. The clerk was also uninterested.

'Well, I guess I got enough to kill an ox,' she thought, and went back to the station.

At home, she put the little vials in the drawer of her dressing-table and stood looking at them with a dreamy tenderness.

'There they are, God bless them,' she said, and she kissed her fingertip and touched each bottle.

The coloured maid was busy in the living-room.

'Hey, Nettie,' Mrs Morse called. 'Be an angel, will you? Run around to Jimmy's and get me a quart of Scotch.'

She hummed while she awaited the girl's return.

During the next few days, whisky ministered to her as tenderly as it had done when she first turned to its aid. Alone, she was soothed and vague, at Jimmy's she was the gayest of the groups. Art was delighted with her.

Then, one night, she had an appointment to meet Art at Jimmy's for an early dinner. He was to leave afterward on a business excursion, to be away for a week. Mrs Morse had been drinking all the afternoon; while she dressed to go out, she felt herself rising pleasurably from drowsiness to high spirits. But as she came out into the street the effects of the whisky deserted her completely, and she was filled with a slow, grinding wretchedness so horrible that she stood swaying on the pavement, unable for a moment to move forward. It was a grey night with spurts of mean, thin snow, and the streets shone with dark ice. As she slowly crossed Sixth Avenue, consciously dragging one foot past the other, a big, scarred horse pulling a rickety express-wagon crashed to his knees before her. The driver swore and screamed and lashed the beast insanely, bringing the whip back over his shoulder for every blow, while the horse struggled to get a footing on the slippery asphalt. A group gathered and watched with interest.

Art was waiting, when Mrs Morse reached Jimmy's.

'What's the matter with you, for God's sake?' was his greeting to her.

'I saw a horse,' she said. 'Gee, I – a person feels sorry for horses. I – it isn't just horses. Everything's kind of terrible, isn't it? I can't help getting sunk.'

'Ah, sunk, me eye,' he said. 'What's the idea of all the bellyaching? What have you got to be sunk about?'

'I can't help it,' she said.

'Ah, help it, me eye,' he said. 'Pull yourself together, will you? Come on and sit down, and take that face off you.'

She drank industriously and she tried hard, but she could not overcome her melancholy. Others joined them and commented on her gloom, and she could do no more for them than smile weakly. She made little dabs at her eyes with her handkerchief, trying to time her movements so they would be unnoticed, but several times Art caught her and scowled and shifted impatiently in his chair.

When it was time for him to go to his train, she said she would leave, too, and go home.

'And not a bad idea, either,' he said. 'See if you can't sleep yourself out of it. I'll see you Thursday. For God's sake, try and cheer up by then, will you?'

'Yeah,' she said. 'I will.'

In her bedroom, she undressed with a tense speed wholly unlike her usual slow uncertainty. She put on her night-gown, took off her hair-net and passed the comb quickly through her dry, varicoloured hair. Then she took the two little vials from the drawer and carried them into the bathroom. The splintering misery had gone from her, and she felt the quick excitement of one who is about to receive an anticipated gift.

She uncorked the vials, filled a glass with water and stood before the mirror, a tablet between her fingers. Suddenly she bowed graciously to her reflection, and raised the glass to it.

'Well, here's mud in your eye,' she said.

The tablets were unpleasant to take, dry and powdery and sticking obstinately half-way down her throat. It took her a long time to swallow all twenty of them. She stood watching her reflection with deep, impersonal interest, studying the movements of the gulping throat. Once more she spoke aloud.

'For God's sake, try and cheer up by Thursday, will you?' she said. 'Well, you know what he can do. He and the whole lot of them.'

She had no idea how quickly to expect effect from the veronal. When she had taken the last tablet, she stood uncertainly, wondering, still with a courteous, vicarious interest, if death would strike her down then and there. She felt in no way strange, save for a slight stirring of sickness from the effort of swallowing the tablets, nor did her reflected face look at all different. It would not be immediate, then; it might even take an hour or so.

She stretched her arms high and gave a vast yawn.

'Guess I'll go to bed,' she said. 'Gee, I'm nearly dead.'

That struck her as comic, and she turned out the bathroom

light and went in and laid herself down in her bed, chuckling softly all the time.

'Gee, I'm nearly dead,' she quoted. 'That's a hot one!'

III

Nettie, the coloured maid, came in late the next afternoon to clean the apartment, and found Mrs Morse in her bed. But then, that was not unusual. Usually, though, the sounds of cleaning waked her, and she did not like to wake up. Nettie, an agreeable girl, had learned to move softly about her work.

But when she had done the living-room and stolen in to tidy the little square bedroom, she could not avoid a tiny clatter as she arranged the objects on the dressing-table. Instinctively, she glanced over her shoulder at the sleeper, and without warning a sickly uneasiness crept over her. She came to the bed and stared down at the woman lying there.

Mrs Morse lay on her back, one flabby, white arm flung up, the wrist against her forehead. Her stiff hair hung untenderly along her face. The bed covers were pushed down, exposing a deep square of soft neck and a pink night-gown, its fabric worn uneven by many launderings; her great breasts, freed from their tight confiner, sagged beneath her armpits. Now and then she made knotted, snoring sounds, and from the corner of her open mouth to the blurred turn of her jaw ran a lane of crusted spittle.

'Mis' Morse,' Nettie called. 'O Mis' Morse! It's terrible late.'

Mrs Morse made no move.

'Mis' Morse,' said Nettie. 'Look, Mis' Morse. How'm I goin' get this bed made?'

Panic sprang upon the girl. She shook the woman's hot shoulder.

'Ah, wake up, will yuh?' she whined. 'Ah, please wake up.'

Suddenly the girl turned and ran out in the hall to the elevator door, keeping her thumb firm on the black, shiny button until the elderly car and its Negro attendant stood before her. She poured a jumble of words over the boy, and led him back to the apartment. He tiptoed creakingly in to the bedside; first gingerly, then so lustily that he left marks in the soft flesh, he prodded the unconscious woman.

'Hey, there!' he cried, and listened intently, as for an echo.

'Jeez. Out like a light,' he commented.

At his interest in the spectacle, Nettie's panic left her. Importance was big in both of them. They talked in quick, unfinished whispers, and it was the boy's suggestion that he fetch the young doctor who lived on the ground floor. Nettie hurried along with him. They looked forward to the limelit moment of breaking their news of something untoward, something pleasurably unpleasant. Mrs Morse had become the medium of drama. With no ill wish to her, they hoped that her state was serious, that she would not let them down by being awake and normal on their return. A little fear of this determined them to make the most, to the doctor, of her present condition. 'Matter of life and death' returned to Nettie from her thin store of reading. She considered startling the doctor with the phrase.

The doctor was in and none too pleased at interruption. He wore a yellow and blue striped dressing-gown, and he was lying on his sofa, laughing with a dark girl, her face scaly with inexpensive powder, who perched on the arm. Half-emptied highball glasses stood beside them, and her coat and hat were neatly hung up with the comfortable implication of a long stay. Always something, the doctor grumbled. Couldn't let anybody alone after a hard day. But he put some bottles and instruments into a case, changed his dressing-gown for his coat and started out with the Negroes.

'Snap it up there, big boy,' the girl called after him. 'Don't be all night.'

The doctor strode loudly into Mrs Morse's flat and on to the bedroom, Nettie and the boy right behind him. Mrs Morse had not moved; her sleep was as deep, but soundless, now. The doctor looked sharply at her, then plunged his thumbs into the lidded pits above her eyeballs and threw his weight upon them. A high, sickened cry broke from Nettie.

'Look like he tryin' to push her right on th'ough the bed,' said the boy. He chuckled.

Mrs Morse gave no sign under the pressure. Abruptly the doctor abandoned it, and with one quick movement swept the covers down to the foot of the bed. With another he flung her night-gown back and lifted the thick, white legs, cross-hatched with blocks of tiny, iris-coloured veins. He pinched them repeatedly, with long, cruel nips, back of the knees. She did not awaken.

'What's she been drinking?' he asked Nettie, over his shoulder.

With the certain celerity of one who knows just where to lay hands on a thing, Nettie went into the bathroom, bound for the cupboard where Mrs Morse kept her whisky. But she stopped at the sight of the two vials, with their red and white labels, lying before the mirror. She brought them to the doctor.

'Oh, for the Lord Almighty's sweet sake!' he said. He dropped Mrs Morse's legs, and pushed them impatiently across the bed. 'What did she want to go taking that tripe for? Rotten yellow trick, that's what a thing like that is. Now we'll have to pump her out, and all that stuff. Nuisance, a thing like that is; that's what it amounts to. Here, George, take me down in the elevator. You wait here, maid. She won't do anything.'

'She won't die on me, will she?' cried Nettie.

'No,' said the doctor. 'God, no. You couldn't kill her with an axe.'

IV

After two days, Mrs Morse came back to consciousness, dazed at first, then with a comprehension that brought with it the slow, saturating wretchedness.

'O Lord, O Lord,' she moaned, and tears for herself and for life striped her cheeks.

Nettie came in at the sound. For two days she had done the ugly, incessant tasks in the nursing of the unconscious, for two nights she had caught broken bits of sleep on the living-room couch. She looked coldly at the big, blown woman in the bed.

'What you been tryin' to do, Mis' Morse?' she said. 'What kine o' work is that, takin' all that stuff?'

'O Lord,' moaned Mrs Morse, again, and she tried to cover her eyes with her arms. But the joints felt stiff and brittle, and she cried out at their ache.

'Tha's no way to ack, takin' them pills,' said Nettie. 'You can thank you' stars you heah at all. How you feel now?'

'Oh, I feel great,' said Mrs Morse. 'Swell, I feel.'

Her hot, painful tears fell as if they would never stop.

'Tha's no way to take on, cryin' like that,' Nettie said. 'After what you done. The doctor, he says he could have you arrested, doin' a thing like that. He was fit to be tied, here.'

'Why couldn't he let me alone?' wailed Mrs Morse. 'Why the hell couldn't he have?'

'Tha's terr'ble, Mis' Morse, swearin' an' talkin' like that,' said Nettie, 'after what people done for you. Here I ain' had no sleep at all for two nights, an' had to give up goin' out to my other ladies!'

'Oh, I'm sorry, Nettie,' she said. 'You're a peach. I'm sorry I've given you so much trouble. I couldn't help it. I just got sunk. Didn't you ever feel like doing it? When everything looks just lousy to you?'

'I wouldn' think o' no such thing,' declared Nettie. 'You got to cheer up. Tha's what you got to do. Everybody's got their troubles.'

'Yeah,' said Mrs Morse. 'I know.'

'Come a pretty picture card for you,' Nettie said. 'Maybe that will cheer you up.'

She handed Mrs Morse a postcard. Mrs Morse had to cover one eye with her hand, in order to read the message; her eyes were not yet focusing correctly.

It was from Art. On the back of a view of the Detroit Athletic Club he had written: 'Greeting and salutations. Hope you have lost that gloom. Cheer up and don't take any rubber nickels. See you on Thursday.'

She dropped the card to the floor. Misery crushed her as if she were between great smooth stones. There passed before her a slow, slow pageant of days spent lying in her flat, of evenings at Jimmy's being a good sport, making herself laugh and coo at Art and other Arts; she saw a long parade of weary horses and shivering beggars and all beaten, driven, stumbling things. Her feet throbbed as if she had crammed them into the stubby champagne-coloured slippers. Her heart seemed to swell and harden.

'Nettie,' she cried, 'for Heaven's sake pour me a drink, will you?'

The maid looked doubtful.

'Now you know, Mis' Morse,' she said, 'you been near daid. I don' know if the doctor he let you drink nothin' yet.'

'Oh, never mind him,' she said. 'You get me one, and bring in the bottle. Take one yourself.'

'Well,' said Nettie.

She poured them each a drink, deferentially leaving hers in the bathroom to be taken in solitude, and brought Mrs Morse's glass in to her.

Mrs Morse looked into the liquor and shuddered back from its odour. Maybe it would help. Maybe, when you had been knocked cold for a few days, your very first drink would give you a lift. Maybe whisky would be her friend again. She prayed without addressing a God, without knowing a God. Oh, please, please, let her be able to get drunk, please keep her always drunk.

She lifted the glass.

'Thanks, Nettie,' she said. 'Here's mud in your eye.'

The maid giggled. 'That's the way, Mis' Morse,' she said. 'You cheer up, now.'

'Yeah,' said Mrs Morse. 'Sure.'

INDEX OF FIRST LINES OF POEMS